# The Art and Practice of Hypnotic Induction

*Favorite Methods of Master Clinicians*

**Edited by Mark P. Jensen, PhD**

Book cover design by Liza Brown (Modern Art Media)
Published by Denny Creek Press, Kirkland, WA 98033 www.dennycreekpress.info
Library of Congress has cataloged this edition as follows:
The art and practice of hypnotic induction: Favorite methods of master clinicians/
Mark P. Jensen, editor.
Includes bibliographic references
1. Hypnotism—Therapeutic Use 2. Psychotherapy

PRINT ISBN: 978-1-9468-3201-6
SMASHWORDS ISBN: 978-1-3705-0888-4

978-1-9468-3202-3
Library of Congress Control Number: 2017936304

*To Lisa,*
*My partner in all things adventurous*

# CONTRIBUTORS

**Allan M. Cyna, FRCA, FANZCA, PhD**
Women's and Children's Hospital
University of Adelaide
Adelaide, SA, Australia, and
Nepean Hospital, University of Sydney
Sydney, NSW, Australia
allan.cyna@sa.gov.au

**Gabor Filo, DDS, FAGD, ABHD, FASCH, FPFA**
Private Practice
Hamilton, ON, Canada
gfilo@cogeco.ca

**Mark P. Jensen, PhD, FASCH**
University of Washington
Seattle, WA, USA
mjensen@uw.edu

**Daniel P. Kohen, MD, FAAP, ABMH**
National Pediatric Hypnosis Training Institute (NPHTI)
University of Minnesota
Minneapolis, MN USA
dpkohen@umn.edu

**Stephen R. Lankton, LCSW, DAHB, FASCH**
Private Practice
Phoenix, AZ, USA
steve@lankton.com

**Julie H. Linden, PhD**
Private Practice
Philadelphia, PA, & Rangely, ME, USA
julie@drjulielinden.com

**Camillo Loriedo, MD, PhD**
Sapienza University of Rome
Rome, Italy
camillo.loriedo@gmail.com

**Bernhard Trenkle, Dipl Psych**
Milton Erickson Institut Rottweil
Rottweil, Germany
mail@bernhard-trenkle.de

**Katalin Varga, PhD**
Eötvös Loránd University
Budapest, Hungry
varga.katalin@ppk.elte.hu

**David M. Wark, PhD, ABPH**
University of Minnesota
Minneapolis, MN, USA
wark@umn.edu

**Michael D. Yapko, PhD.**
Private Practice
Fallbrook, CA, USA
michael@yapko.com

# CONTENTS

# CHAPTER 1

# Introduction

### Mark P. Jensen

*Hypnotic induction* has been defined as the "… procedure designed to induce hypnosis" (Elkins et al., 2015, p. 283) and is provided as a part of hypnosis treatment before clinical suggestions. It is a key component of hypnosis and hypnotic treatments, and is included in virtually all definitions of hypnosis (e.g., Barnier & Nash, 2008; Elkins, Barabasz, Council, & Spiegel, 2015; Green, Barabasz, Barrett, & Montgomery, 2005).

Hypnotic inductions serve many purposes. They establish the context for hypnosis by providing a transition from everyday circumstances to the hypnotic context (Woody & Sadler, 2016). They can also be used to "seed" the ideas that will be included in the clinical suggestions that follow the induction, enhance rapport, and generate or increase positive outcome expectancies, all of which can then enhance patient response to the clinical suggestions (Woody & Sadler, 2016).

However, not all inductions are equally effective for all individuals; people vary in their responses to hypnosis in general and hypnotic inductions in particular (Terhune & Cardeña, 2016). Moreover, there is a lack of consensus among experts regarding what constitutes the essential feature(s) of an effective hypnotic induction. There is also very limited empirical research focusing on hypnotic inductions, and the research that is available has provided somewhat contradictory results.

For example, although there is consistent evidence that the use of hypnotic inductions increases responsiveness to the suggestions that follow, the average increase in response has been found to be only modest in research studies (Braffman & Kirsch, 1999; Hilgard & Tart, 1966). One of the reasons for these modest effects may be the use of scripted inductions in this research. Scripted inductions ignore individual differences in those who receive them. Consistent with this idea, when the individual responses in these studies are examined closely, a great deal of variability is observed. In one study, for example, the same scripted induction resulted in an increase in response to suggestions in 45% of participants, but a *decrease* in response to suggestions in 25% of the sample (Braffman & Kirsch, 1999).

A reasonable hypothesis consistent with these findings is that the efficacy of an induction—that is, the extent to which it increases response to clinical suggestions that follow—is context dependent. For example, response may depend in part on the clinician's skill in tailoring the induction to a particular patient (Barber, 1991). Empirical support exists for this idea. Barabasz and colleagues found that the participants in a study of smoking cessation who were treated by clinicians experienced in the use of hypnosis evidenced over four times more treatment response than participants who were treated by clinical psychology interns with minimal training (Barabasz, Baer, Sheehan, & Barabasz, 1986). Although this finding regarding the role of clinician experience in patient response may seem intuitively obvious, clinician experience has *not* been found to play a role in outcome for many other (nonhypnotic) psychological therapies (Berman & Norton, 1985; Durlak, 1979; Shapiro & Shapiro, 1982; Stein & Lambert, 1984).

Additional support for the importance of tailoring an induction specifically to the patient comes from two other studies performed by Arreed Barabasz and colleagues. In the first of these studies, 20 individuals were given suggestions for age regression by the same highly experienced clinician. However, a scripted induction was used for half of the participants. The other participants were given a tailored induction. Although both groups responded to the hypnotic suggestions, the participants assigned to the tailored induction condition evidenced stronger effects (Barabasz & Christensen, 2006). In the second study, patients with irritable bowel syndrome were provided either tailored or manualized inductions prior to hypnotic suggestions for symptom management (Barabasz & Barabasz, 2006). As with the age regression study, the investigators found that all of the study participants responded to the hypnotic suggestions to some degree. However, only the participants in the tailored condition reported no incapacitating pain at posttreatment. Moreover, the tailored group continued to improve and evidenced better outcomes than the manualized participants at 10 months posttreatment.

Thus, in order to maximize the chances that clients and patients will benefit from hypnotic treatment, clinicians would do well to learn—and then use as appropriate—a *variety* of hypnotic inductions. Use of the same induction for every patient or a small subset of the same inductions would likely result in less efficacy than use of a variety of inductions that are matched to the needs and goals of each client. In addition, clinicians should tailor, based on their experience and training, each of the inductions in their tool chests. Joseph Barber's "Locksmith" metaphor is useful here (Barber, 1991). Clinicians can be constantly asking themselves, "What induction does this particular patient need at this particular time to gain the most benefit from this particular session?" For example, a patient evidencing a need for control might benefit most from permissive language ("You might start to notice...") or from an induction like the one described by Bernhard Trenkle in Chapter 11 of this volume, while a patient who is asking for direction may benefit most from more directive language ("You find yourself in your favorite place...") (Barber, 1991).

Clinicians should also closely observe the patient's response during the induction. They should be asking themselves if there is evidence that the induction is effective, as shown by a particularly strong response to the clinical suggestions and/or signs of an increased depth of trance. If so, then the induction should probably continue as it is being presented. When or if there is evidence that the induction may not be effective (e.g., signs of agitation, anxiety, or discomfort), the clinician can shift gears or obtain and then incorporate feedback from the patient in order to facilitate a more effective induction.

Clinicians would do well to be aware of the research that has been performed in this area that provides empirical guidance regarding factors that may contribute to more effective inductions. This research has been recently and carefully reviewed by Terhune and Cardeña (2016). It suggests, for example, that using the word *hypnosis* during the induction results in greater responsivity to suggestions than not using this word (Gandhi & Oakley, 2005).

Finally, clinicians should seek out and learn from master clinicians who regularly use hypnosis in their practice.

Although systematic research on hypnotic inductions has not yet confirmed the components that are most effective, highly experienced clinicians can be viewed as performing such research throughout their clinical practice, with hundreds if not thousands of clients during tens of thousands of treatment sessions. These clinicians' behaviors have been effectively shaped by the responses they have observed over their decades of clinical work. When experienced masters are asked to describe their "favorite induction(s)," clinicians would be wise to listen very carefully.

Hence, one of the primary purposes of this book; here, eleven experienced clinicians who work in a large variety of settings were asked to (1) describe the factors that they consider as they design and offer an effective hypnotic induction and then (2) provide a description of one or more examples of their favorite inductions. The goal was to provide new and experienced clinicians who use hypnosis with practical information that they can use to enhance their overall efficacy.

In the first of these chapters (Chapter 2 of this book), Michael Yapko notes that in his view inductions have three primary goals: (1) to engage the client's attention; (2) to catalyze dissociations that define the experience as hypnotic; and (3) to enhance responsiveness to the clinical suggestions that follow. He describes four responses that can be elicited from a client as the induction begins (to get into a comfortable position, to establish a comfortable rate of breathing, to create a narrowing focus of attention, and spontaneous behaviors that can then be utilized during hypnosis). He also cites Jeffrey Zeig's work (*The Induction of Hypnosis: An Ericksonian Elicitation Approach*), which presents a view of the hypnotic induction as an *elicitation* of a hypnotic state (Zeig, 2014). The induction example that Yapko describes utilizes the client's past hypnotic experiences to elicit a readiness to accept and respond to clinical suggestions.

In Chapter 3, Julie Linden emphasizes the importance of therapist-client rapport and attunement as a basis for successful inductions. Consistent with the research supporting the importance of tailoring each induction to the situation and client at hand, she points out that she has never used the same induction in the same way with any client. She then lists a number of critical factors that clinicians can focus on when creating an effective induction. These include, among other things, being aware of the client's goal for the session, the clinician's goal or wish for the client, and being aware of and utilizing what the client is doing or experiencing during the induction. The induction example she presents involves the visualization of, exploration of, and identification with a "grand tree" with which the client "... may be familiar, or perhaps it is a new tree, one you have never seen before." Of course, as a living (and powerful) object, a tree and its parts can be used as metaphors for the client or the issues the client is facing. This makes the induction particularly flexible and allows for significant creativity for the client and clinician alike.

In the fourth chapter, Stephen Lankton discusses the hypnotic induction process from the perspective of his States of Consciousness model (Lankton, 1985, 2015). This involves the utilization of stimuli that have personal meaning to the client, observing the client for signs that he or she is responding appropriately, and tailoring the induction stimuli to fit the trance state desired. He describes a key unconscious process that people use—called a transderivational search—to establish the meaning of a communication, and how clinicians can take advantage of this process to enhance responding. His induction illustrates these principles and provides the reader with a clear example of the use of language to increase a dissociation between conscious and unconscious processes, enhancing the trance experience.

Effective inductions do not necessarily require 10 or even 5 minutes. Gabor Filo is a dentist with a vast amount of experience in the clinical application of rapid hypnotic inductions, which can be particularly useful in noisy and fast-paced clinical settings. In Chapter 5, he presents four such inductions, each of which can be completed in 3 minutes or less.

Although hypnotic inductions often invite the client or patient to close his or her eyes and often include suggestions for feeling relaxed, David Wark knows from experience—supported by research—that neither eye closure nor relaxation are required for an individual to respond to hypnotic suggestions. As he notes in Chapter 6, eyes-open alert inductions can allow the subject to have a greater sense of personal involvement and control in the process. Alert inductions can be particularly helpful in settings or situations that call for active movement and engagement, such as athletic activity, artistic performance, and reading or studying. He outlines seven specific skills that he teaches clients when teaching self-hypnosis using eyes-open alert inductions.

In Chapter 7, Katalin Varga discusses how clinicians can use suggestions in settings where formal hypnotic inductions are often not necessary. In medical settings, when patients are about to undergo complex or life-threatening medical procedures, patients are often already ready to accept and respond to suggestions. She discusses how hypnotic suggestions in this context can take many forms, including objects in the environment and nonverbal messages from health care providers, as well as suggestions that communicate important information and can enhance positive outcomes. The clinical cases she describes provide the reader with specific examples of how to make the most of spontaneous trance states for the patient's benefit.

As Daniel P. Kohen points out in Chapter 8, inductions for children and adolescents should be: (1) tailored to the developmental level of the child or teen; (2) offered in the context of evolving rapport with the child; (3) sensitive to the child's motivation and expectations for change; and (4) evocative of curiosity. In this context, he presents the "3 and 6" induction that he frequently uses with children and adolescents, in part because it is so easy for them to learn and use.

In Chapter 9, Camillo Loriedo presents a model he has developed for matching the induction to the characteristics of the family when using hypnosis in the context of family therapy. He points out that when used with families, hypnosis tends to increase synchronic behaviors among the family members, which is associated with increased family harmony, including an increased ability of the family members to pay attention to and listen to each other. He then introduces and provides examples of four family inductions, each of which is tailored to different types of family-interaction patterns. As each type of family faces different challenges, the inductions include metaphors and suggestions for addressing different issues, which can then facilitate healing.

I present, in Chapter 10, an induction that involves two components that I have found to be particularly useful in individuals with chronic pain: a relaxation component and a "favorite place" component. These are often useful and easy for patients to respond to because many people have experienced feeling relaxed at least at some point in their lives, and many people have a favorite place where they go. As a result, it can be easy for patients to recreate feelings of relaxation and the sense of increased calm associated with their favorite place; feelings that are inconsistent with the suffering often associated with chronic pain. In this way, the inductions can themselves be a part of pain treatment.

In Chapter 11, Bernhard Trenkle discusses and provides an example of an induction that he has found helpful when working with clients who may be initially hesitant to participate in hypnosis treatment. This induction involves telling an adaptation of a classic story about a lion who is hesitant to drink out of a pond because he "sees another lion" in the pond when he attempts to drink. In this chapter, he also discusses what he has found to facilitate the induction process, including utilizing the client's experiences with hypnotic-like activities.

Finally, in Chapter 12, Allan Cyna emphasizes the importance of rapport in hypnotic inductions and utilizing what the patient brings to the encounter as a means of facilitating that rapport—including the utilization of what might initially be viewed as unhelpful thoughts and concerns. He describes and provides examples of two specific inductions that he has found to be very useful in medical settings; for example, when using hypnosis for helping patients be more comfortable during medical procedures.

Earlier in this chapter, I emphasized the importance to clinicians of learning and then practicing a *variety* of hypnotic inductions as a way of increasing treatment efficacy. The numerous inductions presented here represent a wonderfully broad yet thorough set of inductions used by some of the world's most experienced clinicians. They range from being very rapid (3 minutes or less) to lengthier (15 minutes or more). Some nurture an experience of deep and comfortable relaxation—responses that may be particularly helpful to individuals learning to more effectively manage pain. Others encourage a sense of active engagement—a state that may be very useful for success in certain activities such as studying or athletics. Some of the inductions presented were designed for use with children and others with adults; some for use with individuals and others with families. A clinician who understands and can use all of these inductions would be a clinician prepared to offer a variety of alternatives and therefore be better able to select an induction most useful for a variety of patients and situations.

Despite the wide variety of inductions described here, however, there are a number of important principles that underlie *all* of the inductions offered. Virtually every one of the clinicians stated that each patient or client, each setting, and each session goal requires an induction that is tailored to that patient, that setting, and that goal; no two inductions should ever be the same, as explicitly noted by Julie Linden in Chapter 3. This strong recommendation is consistent with the research briefly reviewed at the beginning of this chapter, supporting the use of tailored inductions (and hypnosis treatment) over the use of standardized and scripted inductions and treatment (Barabasz & Barabasz, 2006; Barabasz & Christensen, 2006). Thus, as emphasized by many of the authors, although the induction transcripts provide examples and illustrations of the authors' favorite inductions, these should not be copied verbatim or "read" to clients. Rather, they should be integrated and altered as appropriate to fit the needs of each patient and the goal(s) of treatment.

The clinicians also consistently emphasized the importance of rapport, patient/client motivation, and patient/client expectations for maximizing response to the induction and hypnosis treatment. Many also described the specific strategies they use for developing and nurturing these factors. A majority of the authors utilized the client/patient's breathing as a point of focus during the induction. Many recommended that clinicians set aside time at the end of each session to review with the client or patient his or her experience during the hypnosis session, taking this feedback into account when designing the induction and suggestions for the next session. Almost all of the authors explicitly discussed—and I believe that all implicitly applied—the principle of utilizing what the client or patient brings to the session in the induction as a way of engaging with the client or patient (see also Zeig, 2014).

Four of the authors specifically mentioned that one of the goals of induction was to enhance dissociation; an experience or factor that they thought was either required for a response to hypnotic suggestion or at a minimum enhanced this response. Three of the authors mentioned that they purposefully encourage (and therefore seed the idea of) curiosity in their clients or patients prior to or as a part of the induction as a method of enhancing hypnotic depth and therefore enhancing the response to clinical suggestions. Clinicians would do well to pay close attention to all of these pearls of wisdom.

Research is needed to determine which of the induction components and principles play the largest roles in enhancing response to hypnosis treatment. It may be, for example, that clinician-client rapport is more important than clinician (or client) outcome expectancies; strategies that encourage and nurture dissociation may be more important and effective than those that elicit curiosity. More likely, all of these factors and more will be found to be important, perhaps with each playing a greater or lesser role as a function of the context, the client's characteristics, or specific treatment goal. In the meantime, and as we learn more about how these factors enhance the client or patient's response to hypnotic inductions, it would be useful to keep in mind that the authors of the chapters in this book have over 350 years of combined clinical experience, having seen thousands if not tens of thousands of clients and patients. This represents an incredible depth of knowledge and experience; knowledge and experience that should be carefully considered.

**References**

Barabasz, A., & Barabasz, M. (2006). Effects of tailored and manualized hypnotic inductions for complicated irritable bowel syndrome patients. *International Journal of Clinical and Experimental Hypnosis, 54,* 100-112.

Barabasz, A., & Christensen, C. (2006). Age regression: Tailored versus scripted inductions. *American Journal of Clinical Hypnosis, 48,* 251-261.

Barabasz, A. F., Baer, L., Sheehan, D. V., & Barabasz, M. (1986). A three-year follow-up of hypnosis and restricted environmental stimulation therapy for smoking. *International Journal of Clinical and Experimental Hypnosis, 34,* 169-181.

Barber, J. (1991). The locksmith model: Accessing hypnotic responsiveness. In S. Lynn & J. Rhue (Eds.), *Theories of hypnosis: Current models and perspectives* (pp. 241-274). New York, NY: Guilford.

Barnier, A. J., & Nash, M. R. (2008). Introduction: A roadmap for explanation, a working definition. In M. R. Nash & A. J. Barnier (Eds.), *The Oxford handbook of hypnosis: Theory, research, and practice* (pp. 1-18). New York, NY: Oxford University Press.

Berman, J. S., & Norton, N. C. (1985). Does professional training make a therapist more effective? *Psychological Bulletin, 98,* 401-407.

Braffman, W., & Kirsch, I. (1999). Imaginative suggestibility and hypnotizability: An empirical analysis. *Journal of Personality and Social Psychology, 77,* 578-587.

Durlak, J. A. (1979). Comparative effectiveness of paraprofessional and professional helpers. *Psychological Bulletin, 86,* 80-92.

Elkins, G. R., Barabasz, A. F., Council, J. R., & Spiegel, D. (2015). Advancing research and practice: The revised APA Division 30 definition of hypnosis. *International Journal of Clinical and Experimental Hypnosis, 63,* 1-9.

Gandhi, B., & Oakley, D. A. (2005). Does 'hypnosis' by any other name smell as sweet? The efficacy of 'hypnotic' inductions depends on the label 'hypnosis'. *Consciousness and Cognition, 14,* 304-315.

Green, J. P., Barabasz, A. F., Barrett, D., & Montgomery, G. H. (2005). Forging ahead: The 2003 APA Division 30 definition of hypnosis. *International Journal of Clinical and Experimental Hypnosis, 53,* 259-264.

Hilgard, E. R., & Tart, C. T. (1966). Responsiveness to suggestions following waking and imagination instructions and following induction of hypnosis. *Journal of Abnormal Psychology, 71,* 196-208.

Lankton, S. (1985). A states of consciousness model of Ericksonian hypnosis. In S. Lankton, (Ed.), *Ericksonian monographs, number 1: Elements and dimensions of an Ericksonian approach* (pp. 26-41). New York, NY: Brunner/Mazel.

Lankton, S. (2015). Editorial: A SoC model of hypnosis and induction. *American Journal of Clinical Hypnosis, 57*, 367-377.

Shapiro, D. A., & Shapiro, D. (1982). Meta-analysis of comparative therapy outcome studies: A replication and refinement. *Psychological Bulletin, 92*, 581-604.

Stein, D. M., & Lambert, M. J. (1984). On the relationship between therapist experience and psychotherapy outcome. *Clinical Psychology Review, 4*, 127-142.

Terhune, D. B., & Cardeña, E. (2016). Nuances and uncertainties regarding hypnotic inductions: Toward a theoretically informed praxis. *American Journal of Clinical Hypnosis, 59*, 155-174.

Woody, E., & Sadler, P. (2016). What can a hypnotic induction do? *American Journal of Clinical Hypnosis, 59*, 138-154.

Zeig, J. (2014). *The induction of hypnosis: An Ericksonian elicitation approach.* Phoenix, AZ: The Milton H. Erickson Foundation Press.

# CHAPTER 2

## The Induction of Hypnosis: An Invitation to the Client to Engage... *Deeply*

**Michael D. Yapko**

*Michael D. Yapko, Ph.D., is a clinical psychologist residing near San Diego, California. He is internationally recognized for his work in advancing clinical hypnosis and outcome-focused psychotherapy, routinely teaching to professional audiences all over the world. To date, he has been invited to present his ideas and methods to colleagues in more than 30 countries across six continents and all over the United States.*

*Dr. Yapko is the recipient of numerous major awards for his innovative contributions in advancing the fields of hypnosis and brief therapy, including lifetime achievement awards from the American Psychological Association's Division 30 (Society of Psychological Hypnosis), the International Society of Hypnosis, and the Milton H. Erickson Foundation. Dr. Yapko is the author of 15 books and editor of three others, as well as numerous book chapters and articles on the subjects of hypnosis and the use of strategic psychotherapies.*

*These include his most recent book,* The Discriminating Therapist: Asking "How" Questions, Making Distinctions, and Finding Direction in Therapy, *as well as his widely used hypnosis text,* Trancework: An Introduction to the Practice of Clinical Hypnosis *(4th ed.), and the award-winning* Mindfulness and Hypnosis: The Power of Suggestion to Transform Experience. *He has also produced many CD and DVD programs. His works have been translated into nine languages. More information about Dr. Yapko's teaching schedule and publications can be found on his website:* ***www.yapko.com****.*

* * *

The process of hypnotic induction can be regarded as among the first steps the clinician and client take together to cogenerate a meaningful quality of engagement. An induction process is focused, experiential (rather than merely intellectual), and helps move the therapy session steadily in the direction of mutually agreed-upon therapeutic goals. It is the beginning phase of an ongoing, dynamically evolving therapeutic process, one that will likely strive to facilitate and utilize hypnotic phenomena in line with therapeutic objectives (e.g., age regression, analgesia, time distortion, etc.). Thus, the induction process sets the stage for all that is to follow.

While the specific induction technique the clinician employs matters, what matters even more is achieving the primary aims of the induction. These include: (1) engaging and focusing the client's attention; (2) catalyzing the dissociations that define the client's experience as hypnotic (i.e., detached from usual perceptual cues, increased automaticity of responses, and a "felt sense" of suggested experiences); and (3) building responsiveness for further suggestions as the session continues to unfold (Yapko, 2012).

## Preliminaries to the Induction Process

By the time the clinician invites the client to directly participate in hypnotic experience, at least four things should already have been achieved during the clinical interview. First, the therapeutic relationship should have been defined as both active and multidimensional, thereby making the incorporation of hypnosis into treatment appropriate and relevant. Second, the clinician has characterized the therapeutic interaction as fully collaborative, indicating clearly that he or she will do hypnosis *with* the client, not *to* the client. Third, the therapist will have provided a meaningful rationale for including hypnosis in the treatment process, at the very least highlighting the merits of hypnosis in *creating a context* for greater focus, enhanced learning, and fuller access to one's innate strengths and resources. Fourth, the clinician should have used the interview questions, especially "how" questions, to reveal misinformation or missing information that can be provided and to identify innate resources to be amplified in the treatment.

Effective interview questions can build client curiosity and receptivity while also helping the clinician recognize specific client attributes (e.g., cognitive style, response style, imaginative abilities, previous experience with hypnosis, quality of expectations, etc.) to take into account in deciding on a viable approach to the induction. (For a discussion of the "how" question and ways it can be utilized to help pinpoint meaningful therapeutic targets, see Yapko, 2016, *The Discriminating Therapist.*) Thus, the induction becomes a bridge for smoothly moving from the interview process to building and delivering the hypnotic intervention.

**Assumptions About Hypnotic Inductions**

The classic phrase "inducing hypnosis" implies the clinician is doing something *to* the client. Some approaches to hypnosis reinforce this perspective by using structured techniques (such as a counting technique) that are impersonal. The language of hypnosis is sometimes limiting and even misleading, for the client is not simply a passive receptacle for the clinician's suggestions.

In contrast, a more natural approach called "utilization" features conversational suggestions that encourage the client to generate personally meaningful images or memories as the suggested focus of the induction process. Thus, the client is an active force in shaping the interaction, and the clinician must respond meaningfully to the unique responses of the individual (Yapko, 2015). *Guiding the person into hypnosis* may be a more accurate way to represent the clinician's role in the induction process. In the capacity of guide, one cannot know the exact experience the client is having or is going to have, so giving the client room to experience hypnosis in his or her own unique way is not only desirable but *necessary.* Even as the induction begins, saying something such as, "I don't know what the most comfortable position is for you to sit in right now" indirectly encourages the client to arrange him- or herself comfortably while also affirming his or her power to choose whether and how to respond.

There are as many induction methods as there are practitioners of hypnosis, and each reflects the beliefs about hypnosis a clinician holds as the basis for his or her methods. For example, one primary consideration is whether hypnosis is viewed as something that takes place *intra*personally (i.e., within the person) or whether hypnosis is something that occurs *inter*personally (i.e., between people). When the view of hypnosis is expanded to include an interpersonal lens, encompassing dynamics of social influence that shape the willingness to participate in such experiences (based on such factors as clinician credibility and the client's level of trust), it no longer makes sense to administer either a standardized (i.e., scripted or "one-size-fits-all") technique or formal test of hypnotizability. Instead of assessing the client's hypnotizability as if it were a fixed and measurable trait, it is assumed that hypnotic responsiveness is dynamic and will build as the therapeutic alliance and client engagement in the process intensifies. This viewpoint underlies my more conversational approach to hypnotic induction described later in this chapter.

## Beginning the Hypnotic Process

In beginning an induction, there are certain minimal responses the clinician will likely want from the client, described below. None of these are essential, however, since people can experience hypnosis and generate hypnotic phenomena even while active and alert (see Chapter 6 of this volume). Generally speaking, though, these initial responses are basic to clinical contexts where putting the client at ease and building receptivity to further suggestions are crucial. These include: (1) Suggesting, directly or indirectly, that the client *assume a comfortable physical position* is a good starting point. A general immobility called catalepsy is typical of the hypnotized individual; the extra effort it takes to readjust one's position while in hypnosis makes it necessary to be sure the client is in a comfortable position in which he or she can remain effortlessly over time. He or she can always adjust position, of course, but a little forethought can reduce the need to do so; (2) *Suggesting a comfortable rate of breathing*; it helps to relax people to encourage a slowed, more rhythmically even breathing; (3) *Suggesting the client begin to narrow his or her focus and turn it increasingly inward;* suggesting that the client close his or her eyes at the start is generally a good idea, followed by suggestions for greater attention paid to developing signs of comfort and any other meaningful internal awareness; and (4) *Using whatever experiences or behaviors the client spontaneously offers as a basis for experiencing hypnosis.* This is one aspect of "utilization" in hypnosis and can be accomplished by commenting on client behaviors and tying them to suggestions of relaxation and entering hypnosis (Zeig, 2014). For example, "Each shift in your chair can allow you to be more comfortable... Each breath you take in can further soothe and relax your body..."

With the client growing more comfortable and responsive to the clinician through these preliminaries, the hypnotic induction can now get under way.

## Imposing Versus Eliciting Hypnosis

In the utilization approach described above, hypnosis is viewed as a natural experience occurring routinely in people; it is not a "special state." In adopting this perspective, one of the tasks of the skilled clinician is to recognize hypnotic responses as they naturally occur in the course of ongoing therapeutic interaction and then build on these responses meaningfully in a spontaneous and conversational manner. One might say something such as,

> You've been so focused on those hurtful feelings for so long, it can be a welcome relief to start to focus on some new possibilities... and to help you focus, you can allow your eyes

> to close and listen as I encourage a shift in your awareness.

The hypnosis session proceeds from there. Such an approach differs markedly from saying, "I'm going to name body parts while you focus on relaxing," which represents a structured progressive muscle relaxation or "body scan" technique that varies minimally in delivery across clients. One approach says, in essence, "here's my technique," while the other says, "you have experiences that can be the basis for developing new responses." The former is more imposing an approach while the latter involves more of an elicitation of responses, i.e., the images, internal dialogue, feelings, and behaviors that are personally meaningful and engaging as the basis for the induction and therapy. Jeffrey Zeig (2011) described the distinction in methods this way:

> Initiating hypnotic induction is a little like fostering love. One cannot elicit an emotional state, such as love, by intoning, "Go deeply into love." Similarly, one does not elicit hypnosis by commanding a passive patient, "Go deeply into trance." Note a key word in the previous sentence, *elicit*. Hypnosis is elicited, not induced (despite the label "induction") ... The hypnotherapist establishes conditions that allow the patient to bring forth previously dormant trance components. (p. 45)

The instructions to the client in the conversational (Ericksonian, naturalistic, utilization) approach to hypnotic induction are typically more individualized, permissive, indirect, and process-oriented compared to other, more technique-oriented approaches. Furthermore, there is typically not as clear a beginning, middle, or end to the induction compared to the clearer transitions from phase to phase of the hypnosis session found in more structured approaches.

The stimulus for the hypnotic experience in the utilization approach is found in the conscious and unconscious associations (e.g., cognitive, sensory, emotional, physiological) the clinician elicits in the client through his or her suggestions. This perspective also differs considerably from the view that the power of the hypnotic suggestion is contained in the suggestion itself rather than in the way the client relates to it. Which specific associations of client experience will be triggered by your words cannot be predicted with certainty. Observing and using a client's responses as they arise will, of necessity, temper one's approach.

**Using Past Hypnotic Experiences as the Foundation of Induction**

The recognition that hypnotic experiences arise spontaneously in people allows for a smooth transition from an interview or discussion into the induction phase of hypnosis. Virtually all people have had naturally occurring or spontaneous hypnotic experiences at various times in their lives. They may not necessarily have thought of such experiences as having any relationship to hypnosis, but they can easily be framed as such by the clinician. Orienting people to personal experiences of absorption across daily life experiences associates them to their capacity for becoming engaged, and the induction provides them a means for using that capacity *now*. Of course, if the person is already experienced with, enjoys, and is comfortable with hypnosis, the induction is even easier to perform. Associating the person to those elements of the hypnotic experience they enjoy most (such as the physical and emotional comfort or the freedom to explore new possibilities) serves as the induction procedure described in the following transcript with commentary. It is just one of many possible inductions one might consider employing.

### A Sample Induction with Commentary: Building Upon Past Hypnotic Experiences

**Clinician: I don't know just what the most comfortable position is for you to sit in right now... but I do know that *you* know something about what feels most comfortable for you...**

*[An indirect suggestion to sit comfortably while defining the client, rather than the clinician, as the expert on the client.]*

**so you can arrange yourself in whatever way you'd like... of course, you can rearrange yourself anytime you want to, or need to, as the process goes on...**

*[A suggestion for flexibly adjusting position as necessity may dictate.]*

**and when you're ready, you can let your eyes close...**

*[Permissive suggestion for eye closure...]*

**so you can begin to build the kind of internal focus... that makes it easy for you to grow more relaxed and more attentive over the next few minutes...**

*[Permissive suggestion for focusing and relaxing.]*

**Now, I don't really have to take the time to describe what it feels like to relax... because you already know... and I don't really have to take the time to describe what it's like to get focused because you already know...**

*[Associating to existing knowledge from past experiences as the basis for building relaxation and focus now.]*

**you also know from previous experience what can happen when you allow yourself to gradually become more focused...**

*[Placing the responsibility on the client to allow the experience to build gradually.]*

**and slowly your priorities may begin to shift... from first building a strong sense of comfort... to starting to really enjoy that comfort... from first building a quality of focus... to then starting enjoying that focus...**

*[An indirect suggestion for moving from effortful to effortless, enjoyable experience.]*

**It isn't something that happens all at once... even for the people who are the most skilled at being able to get absorbed in this process of hypnosis...**

*[Emphasizing taking his or her time, i.e., no need to hurry the experience.]*

**after all, your ability differs a little from day to day, circumstance to circumstance, mood to mood.**

*[Reinforcing the experience is dynamic, i.e., changing from one time to another, to prevent becoming rigid regarding about how it's "supposed" to be.]*

**It's one of the nice things about feeling like you have all the time you need to move along at your own comfortable rate...**

*[Again reinforcing the freedom to take however much time he or she needs to develop focus.]*

**it can be a wonderful experience for you to comfortably discover your natural abilities...**

*[Encouraging empowerment.]*

**especially when you can relax knowing that I don't have any particular expectation about how long it should take or how deeply you...**

*[Reinforcing the experience is for your benefit, not to try to please me.]*

**should experience your ever growing comfort and awareness...**

*[Emphasizing comfort and awareness growing over time.]*

**It's such an interesting thing to me, when I begin a hypnosis session like this one... because in one way, I know you... but I really *don't* know you... I don't know your inner world the way you do... all the things that make you unique. How can I possibly predict how you're going to respond to the things I talk about?**

*[Acknowledging again that the client is the expert on his or her experience, not me, avoiding an unnecessary "power struggle."]*

**But as you get more focused...**

*[Presupposition for greater focus.]*

**and as I introduce some important ideas and meaningful possibilities to you... you'll naturally hear many of the helpful things you want to hear...**

*[Presupposition ideas will be important and possibilities will be meaningful.]*

**and some of the things you'll hear are things that you may not even fully grasp just yet that can gradually...**

*[Reassurance that awareness can grow gradually, not necessarily with some big "aha!" moment.]*

**or even suddenly perhaps... make a profound difference in the way that you feel... and the way that you approach things... and the way that you live your life...**

*[Building the expectancy that this experience can be the start of big and meaningful changes.]*

**It's always so interesting to me... how people inevitably move forward from one phase of life... into a new phase of life... and you discover the things that really mattered at one time... that just don't matter anymore... and the things that never used to matter... that now begin to matter a lot... and here at the beginning of this session... you don't really know exactly what...**

*[A truism that associates the client to change being inevitable and encourages personalizing the suggestion with examples from his or her own history.]*

**I'm going to talk about... or exactly what your response is going to be... and that's what can raise your curiosity... because you know as well as I do how important curiosity is in driving the desire to discover new possibilities...**

*[Building a tolerance for ambiguity, a growing sense of curiosity and thus a receptivity to being open to discovery.]*

**perhaps that's why there's something about not knowing at the beginning of a session that, to me, is one of the most compelling aspects of experiencing the deep comfort and strong focus of hypnosis...**

*[Framing "not knowing" as a beneficial catalyst to finding out. "Not knowing" in hypnosis can be an especially powerful driving force for receptivity and finding new personal resources.]*

**the opportunity to discover hidden abilities you didn't know were there... that can delight you when you find them... the ability to get absorbed and really take in ideas in new ways and at deeper levels...**

*[Increased appreciation for the Self.]*

**after all, there's a big difference between knowing something and *realizing* something...**

*[Suggesting that even previously held knowledge can take on a new level of significance.]*

**it's a curious thing to be sitting there and listening... to have narrowed your attention and engaged with me in this way...**

*[Reinforcing attentiveness.]*

**you committed yourself first to the idea of focusing and now the actual experience... and through that commitment, you can discover that you have all the freedom in the world... to listen and learn... absorb and experience...**

*[Suggesting that commitment is a necessary precursor to effective learning and making good use of that learning.]*

**it's what makes it possible for you to notice the inevitable shifts that take place... and there really are lots of shifts that take place... some in your awareness... some outside of your awareness...**

*[A process suggestion to notice shifts taking place in his or her experience that can serve as ratifications and strengtheners of hypnotic experience.]*

**I have no way of knowing at just what moment you begin to realize that your breathing is changing... or that your**

**pulse rate is changing... or that you totally forgot that you're wearing a watch until I remind you...**

*[Suggestions to notice obvious physical shifts as well as shifts in awareness taking place.]*

**it's *time* to be so deeply comfortable...**

*[Using the watch as a deepener.]*

**it can be so soothing to realize how these sensations fade in and fade out of your awareness... and isn't that what a change in awareness is about? Different things that pass through your mind... different sensations that you become aware of and then unaware of...**

*[Ratifying shifts in awareness as foundational to meaningful changes.]*

**an ever changing yet remarkably consistent quality of experience... here is some of what you've been striving to understand... the growth that takes place in you as you learn more about how your own mind works...**

*[Reinforcing the general message that "changes happen" as a precursor to specific changes yet to come in the target area(s).]*

**and how your body works... as you continue to grow as a person... and *outgrow* what just isn't relevant anymore... just as you have outgrown many things over your lifetime that seemed important then that lost their value as you evolved other, better ways of doing things...**

*[Suggesting that as new experiences in therapy accumulate, growth will occur and as growth occurs it will be easier to leave behind old patterns that no longer serve any useful purpose, encouraging the retrieval of personal examples to make the point.]*

The session now progresses into addressing the specific issues that are consistent with achieving the therapeutic objectives.

## Discussion

This conversational induction process addresses the larger aims of *any* hypnotic induction process:

- The induction encourages the client to focus, relax, listen, and absorb.
- The induction references the use of innate skills and past experiences to create a worthwhile experience in the present moment.
- The induction offers suggestions permissively, thereby empowering the client to use his or her own resources rather than merely comply with arbitrary commands.
- The induction establishes the client as the expert on him- or herself, promoting an easy acceptance of his or her own style and rate of responsiveness. There is no unreasonable mandate to "do it right."
- The induction provides many embedded suggestions for comfort to deepen the engagement as the induction unfolds.
- The induction reframes "not knowing" as valuable in generating curiosity, which is framed as an opportunity for personal discovery, thereby building greater responsiveness.
- The induction provides a realistic basis for believing that change is possible, even inevitable, and encourages a personal identification with that concept.

## Conclusion

There are many, many ways to conduct an induction of hypnosis, ranging from structured to conversational. *Anything* that engages the client's attention, builds receptivity, and encourages a meaningful participation in the process can be considered an effective induction. Thus, the client's response determines the value of the induction. Using the client's own past experience as the basis for the induction as described here may make it easier to engage in the induction process.

As one's knowledge about and experience with hypnosis grows, it becomes ever more apparent that people have many more resources than they may realize. The experience of hypnosis can provide a focused context for discovering and using these resources in the best of ways. An absorbing hypnotic induction process provides the pathway into these empowering experiences.

## References

Yapko, M. (2012). *Trancework: An introduction to the practice of clinical hypnosis* (4th ed.). New York, NY: Routledge.

Yapko, M. (2015). *Essentials of hypnosis* (2nd ed.). New York, NY: Routledge.

Yapko, M. (2016). *The discriminating therapist: Asking "how" questions, making distinctions, and finding direction in therapy.* Fallbrook, CA: Yapko Publications.

Zeig, J. (2011). Hypnotic induction. In C. Loriedo, J. Zeig, & G. Nardone (Eds.), *Tranceforming Ericksonian methods* (pp. 43-58). Phoenix, AZ: The Milton H. Erickson Foundation Press.

Zeig, J. (2014). *The induction of hypnosis: An Ericksonian elicitation approach*. Phoenix, AZ: The Milton H. Erickson Foundation Press.

**For Further Reading...**

Gafner, G. (2006). *More hypnotic inductions*. New York, NY: Norton.

Gafner, G., & Benson, S. (2000). *Handbook of hypnotic inductions*. New York, NY: Norton.

Jensen, M. (2011). *Hypnosis for chronic pain management* (Both the therapist guide and patient workbook). Oxford, UK: Oxford University Press.

Lyons, L. (2015). *Using hypnosis with children: Creating and delivering effective interventions*. New York, NY: Norton.

Weitzenhoffer, A. (2000). *The practice of hypnotism* (2nd ed.). New York, NY: John Wiley & Sons.

Yapko, M. (2012). *Trancework: An introduction to the practice of clinical hypnosis* (4th ed.). New York, NY: Routledge.

Yapko, M. (1992). *Hypnosis and the treatment of depression*. New York, NY: Brunner/Mazel.

Yapko, M. (1994). *Suggestions of abuse: True and false memories of childhood sexual trauma*. New York, NY: Simon & Schuster.

Yapko, M. (1997). *Focusing on feeling good*. A self-management audio CD program for overcoming depression. Fallbrook, CA: Yapko Publications.

Yapko, M. (2001). *Treating depression with hypnosis: Integrating cognitive-behavioral and strategic approaches*. New York, NY: Brunner/Routledge.

Yapko, M. (2005). *Sleeping soundly: Enhancing sleep with hypnosis* (Audio CD program). Fallbrook, CA: Yapko Publications.

Yapko, M. (Ed.)(2006). *Hypnosis and treating depression: Applications in clinical practice*. New York, NY: Routledge.

Yapko, M. (2008). *Calm down! A self-help program for managing anxiety*. (Audio CD program.) Fallbrook, CA: Yapko Publications.

Yapko, M. (2011). *Mindfulness and hypnosis: The power of suggestion to transform experience*. New York, NY: Norton.

Zeig, J. (2011). Hypnotic induction. In C. Loriedo, J. Zeig & G. Nardone (Eds.), *Tranceforming Ericksonian methods* (pp. 43-58). Phoenix, AZ: The Milton H. Erickson Foundation Press.

Zeig, J. (2014). *The induction of hypnosis: An Ericksonian elicitation approach*. Phoenix, AZ: The Milton H. Erickson Foundation Press.

# CHAPTER 3

# The "Tree Exploration" Induction: The Use of Archetypes to Evoke Affect

**Julie H Linden**

*Julie H. Linden, clinical psychologist, is a past president of the International Society of Hypnosis (ISH). Both the beginning and end of her presidency were marked by the two largest scientific hypnosis congresses in the history of ISH, with more than 2500 participants from 56 countries contributing to their success. Long before integrative medicine was popular, she was integrating hypnosis principles and skills into a wide range of areas. In medical settings, she was an early (1975) pioneer of pediatric hypnotic pain management and facilitating healing in both acute care (e.g., burn patients, medical procedures, emergency room presentations, and preparation for surgery), as well as chronic illness care (e.g., kidney dialysis, oncology, cystic fibrosis, to name a few).*

*In clinical psychology, she has forged the path on the integration of play therapy, trauma, and hypnosis. Julie works with clients of all ages and has contributed to the understanding of hypnotic work in a developmental framework. Her varied interests and writings range from children and adolescents; trauma, hypnotic sandtray; gender-sensitive hypnosis and feminist hypnotherapy; ego state therapy; hypnosis and creativity; hypnosis and the brain-gut connection; education and training in hypnosis; as well as hypnosis and leadership.*

*Passionate about hypnosis best describes Julie, as she enthusiastically travels the world, lecturing and training others on the enormous potential for healthy change when hypnosis is incorporated into one's health care practice.*

* * *

Learning how to *do* an induction in hypnosis is easy. There are countless inductions that have been written that you can read or memorize, including those in this book. Some of the readers may find it helpful to do just that at the start of their hypnosis training. Reading others' inductions provides ideas and practice, just as an art student may hone his or her skills by copying the masters. Learning how *to create* an induction and *how to apply* hypnotic principles to an induction is a lifetime learning experience, much enhanced by the stumbling mistakes we make along our learning journey. Dabney Ewin's *101 Things I Wish I'd Known When I Started Using Hypnosis* (Ewin, 2009) is a good example of a compendium of ideas one only learns through the trial and error of empiricism. The art of creating inductions is similarly improved by the fine-tuning that comes from the cycle of experimenting, evaluating, dialoguing, and reinventing.

Before any successful induction is the establishment of the hypnotic relationship, based on trust, attunement, empathy, presence, kindness, sensitivity, and responsiveness. If we are attuned and "listening" to all that our client is communicating, including and perhaps especially the nonverbal communications, then we can follow the lead of the client whose unconscious usually knows what she or he needs. The client does not typically overtly choose the images, sensory elements, words, metaphors, and narratives of the induction the practitioner uses. The client may tell you their favorite places, activities, pleasant memories, and meaningful sensory events, but the organization and content of the suggestions housed in an induction are built by the practitioner. In this mode, being attentive to our interoceptive sensations and instincts will also guide our creative process.

An induction is simply a vehicle for delivering suggestions, whether to oneself or by the clinician. For some clinicians, the induction is the act of helping someone find their attentive and absorbed trance moment. It is a tool only, and its content is far less important than the relationship, which provides the container, the holding environment, for the client in which she or he explores the route to change. This is probably why so much has been written on the patient-clinician relationship and the spontaneous trance that occurs in most forms of psychotherapy.

It is worthwhile to note that if you do not like a client or feel ill at ease with them and, of course, *vice versa,* a trusting relationship may not form. Without this relationship, hypnosis is unlikely to be useful. This realm of why we do or do not connect with a client is fuel for supervision or consultation and a reminder that we cannot be all things to all clients. The more we learn about *being hypnotic* with a client rather than *doing hypnosis,* the more likelihood that a relationship will form and pave the way for the client's successful outcome.

This notion of *being hypnotic* means different things to different practitioners. For me, it is about being fully present as I accompany a client on their journey to positive change.

As their companion, I bring with me all of my biopsychosocial knowledge, professional training, and life experience and in the intimate and sacred place of our treatment contract utilize *what works* to support the desired change. This notion of *what works* underlies the comment on evaluating hypnotic inductions. Feedback from the client and evidence of the desired change are determinants of *what works*. *Being hypnotic* is being receptive, neutral, empowering, ego-strengthening, and embodying. It both leads to and follows the establishment of the therapeutic relationship. For those who work hypnotically with children, *being hypnotic* also means that you enter the imaginative and playful world of the child, while remaining aware of where they are developmentally.

However, I do not want to imply that the relationship alone will lead to useful suggestions without some thought given to the type of induction. The vehicle matters. If crossing the Atlantic Ocean in a canoe, we are less likely to reach our destination successfully; certainly, it would be a more arduous trip. I have known clinicians who always use the same induction, over and over. I am at the other end of the continuum and believe I have never used the same induction in the same way. As a psychotherapist who appreciates that every client relationship is one of a kind, it follows that each induction can be uniquely framed for the unique individual with whom I am working, shaped by my attunement to their needs, goals, and preferences.

The art of suggestion takes many forms, from direct forms such as "You will feel better and better every day, less and less anxious, more and more calm," to those that use metaphors, storytelling, indirect communications, and double binds. All of these types of inductions are taught in most basic hypnosis curricula. These basic forms are helpful to learn and know; we enrich the client's choices and ours when we have numerous tools in our therapeutic armamentarium. For example, some clients cannot visualize, and guided imagery frustrates them. Others dislike stories and indirect styles and want to be told what to do.

The more techniques you master, the more skill you will have in eliciting responses that help others. In my experience, the "voice" and style you develop utilizing hypnosis must be your own. But every personalized induction is necessarily a new creation. Each person's uniqueness requires a novel approach. In another sense, there are no new inductions, only endless ways of composing, arranging, and delivering timeless suggestions for wellness, wellbeing, healing, and growth.

So, metaphorically speaking, choose your vehicle (induction), load it with the equipment (suggestions) for your passenger, and then drive (personalize, pace) the vehicle where the client needs to go. With children, the vehicle may be a magic carpet, more motorically active and less formal, but the suggestions and personalization are still essential ingredients.

There are several key elements I focus on when choosing and creating a formal induction. Most of these elements are also important in spontaneous, informal and indirect trance work.

1. What is the goal the client has set? How does the patient "sense" that goal? How will the patient know she or he has achieved the goal?
2. What is my goal/wish for the patient? (Again, with all of the senses.)
3. Is this a "learning about hypnosis" induction or an induction for deeper work and suggestions?

4. What is the client doing right now? I often start an induction with where the client is, noticing, observing, naming in order to ground the client, communicate my attunement, and to confirm (or not) their mood, affect, and energy. What I choose to focus on in this moment is typically NOT what is distressing a client. For example, if I am working with a client who has a cold, is asthmatic, or in some way hampered in breathing, I will not choose to focus on their breathing. I am more likely to refocus their attention away from the body, initially, and find elements of their environment such as noticing the room they are in, its sounds, and light while inviting curiosity of what is outside the body.
5. What corrective perceptions, cognitions, and experiences do I think will assist the patient? (Or what perceptions, cognitions, etc. do I believe are limiting the patient?)
6. What are the interests, images, and memories that the patient has reported with emotionally positive valence? Starting with positive feelings facilitates hope and optimism. This is motivating for most clients. (We want to know the emotionally negative images, memories, sensorial experiences, as well, since they provide the material for the deeper work of suggestions that will be used for corrective experiences.)
7. Will some form of trance ratification be useful for the client?
8. How much time do I have for the induction? (While the induction of breathing and progressive muscle relaxation can take minutes, the timing of uncovering work is often unpredictable!) Is there time for the

important postinduction "debriefing" and feedback? In psychotherapy, I like to use the sandwich approach during a session: recap the important events since last session, decide the day's goal of the formal hypnosis, make the suggestions, and evaluate the experience with the client. Initiating a posthypnotic suggestion for rapid trance reinduction is useful to provide more time for the deeper suggestive work.

9. Will ideo-motor signaling facilitate the hypnotic induction experience? (If so, teach that first.)
10. Do I want to include a posthypnotic suggestion?
11. How will I access the client's affect, match it and intensify the experience for the successful outcome? There is no change unless affect is stimulated.
12. What images, senses, thoughts are in *my* mind about the client? And why might they be there?

With these considerations in mind, I begin an induction. Although the work of a seasoned clinician can look deceptively effortless, it is important to note (based on the considerations listed above) how much the clinician is holding in mind (and body!) as she or he creates places of change for someone in a trance state.

The induction I have chosen to share in this chapter, when offered to a client in a comfortable trance state, typically feels like a living, breathing entity. (Perhaps my vehicle is Puff, the Magic Dragon?) I have utilized it in countless settings always with the surprising feedback from people that they have experienced it as being one of the most moving or most deepening inductions they have ever experienced. This induction reliably evokes significant personal material that proves therapeutically useful for the client. My conclusion is that the feedback has as much to do with the relationship of attunement and trust as with the inner work stimulated and produced by the archetypes within this induction.

## "Tree Exploration" Induction with Commentary

This induction can be used for a variety of psychotherapeutic objectives, such as embodiment and body awareness, developing empathy, building resilience, for ego-strengthening as well as for some diagnostic exploration of ego-strength and trauma history. One can begin with any induction such as eye focus, breathing, progressive relaxation, or a naturalistic movement into the trance state followed by this induction. Sometimes it is useful to take someone to his or her safe place and then proceed with the following imagery.

**Clinician: And as you look around, you will notice a path stretching out before you that you had not seen before.**

*[The comment "you had not seen before" creates curiosity and increases attentiveness and motivates expectancy effects.]*

**It may be a grass path, one made of moss, or pebbles, dirt or sand... I don't know what kind of path it is, but you'll know.**

**It may be a familiar path, from your past or future, or one you create now that is just right for you at this moment.**

**And you are curious about this path and where it will lead you. So you follow the path.**

*[Lots of choice about this path keeps the client focused on perceptual content, while your suggestions aid the subconscious to search for historical associations.]*

**As you walk along, you feel the imprint that your footsteps make on the ground beneath you. You notice the feel of each step as the ground comes up to meet your feet and support your movement. It may be soft or firm beneath each footstep, and you become aware of how the sole of each foot meets mother earth. You may even sense the earth's energy entering each foot, and flowing through your body, energizing, restoring, regenerating with each step. It is a slow, comfortable walk along the path.**

**You notice the rhythm of your amble, the effortless orchestration of feet, legs, arms, and breath, without even needing to think about it.**

*[More body awareness, and ego-strengthening.]*

**You notice the time of day, the play of light, the smells of the outdoors, the temperature and weather...**

*[Awakening all of the senses.]*

**and the ease of moving along this path at your own pace and location. Soon you come to a very large tree directly in front of you on your pathway.**

*[Empowerment—this is the client's journey, not yours.]*

**This tree is quite grand. It may be a tree with which you are familiar, or perhaps it is a new tree, one you have never seen before. Take some time to examine this tree. Notice its large trunk, so very wide you are unable to reach your arms around its girth. Notice how high its limbs and branches reach into the sky. Your head leans back to see all the way to the top.**

**And as high as these branches reach into the sky, that is how deep the root structure is which reaches deep into the earth.**

*[Links to body memories, often with spontaneous regression to childhood and those things that were bigger.]*

**You wonder about the deep roots that nourish the tree, through which flow the water and nutrients that grow the tree and keep it healthy.**

*[Metaphor for one's own roots, need for nourishment, what creates health.]*

**You sit under the magnificent branches of this grand tree, perhaps leaning your back against its sturdy trunk.**

**You wonder, imagine, and reflect on the many seasons this tree has lived and survived.**

[I use the term "survived" when wanting to seed suggestions to move from victim stance to victor stance.]

**What has mother nature dealt this tree? You wonder how it has experienced the heat of summer, excessive sunshine? Has it suffered droughts and dry spells, while providing shade to those who sat beneath its broad and protective branches; how in the fall it shed its leaves or needles, weathered the winds and rains, bending with the hurricane forces, sometimes losing limbs, yet managing to right itself when the quiet returned; how it faced the cold of winter, branches laden with the heavy snow and ice, nature's pruning, leaving it with scars where limbs once resided; and how each spring it burst forth with new growth, triumphantly sending forth blossoms, new leaves, tiny twigs of hope of more growth.**

*[Be careful—some will imagine deciduous trees and others, coniferous trees, so be general or allow for both possibilities. The more accurately your suggestions match the internal experience of the client, the more trust is established. It is this component*

*that creates the response of "How did you know I was... (fill in the blank)?" from the client.]*

**And as you think about the tree and imagine the many seasons it has weathered, you sense a kinship with this tree.**

*[This facilitates mentalization, self-reflection.]*

**You wonder how alike and different you and this tree are. You notice the way in which your roots run deep, the shape of the stance you hold in the world, the sources of your nourishment, the experiences you have weathered.**

*[Here you can make suggestions specific to your client, such as ego-enhancing statements; for example, "...You notice how you are free to move in the world, unlike the tree which stays always in one place;" or, "You notice the way you can provide shelter to those around you part of the time, like the tree who sheds its leaves and sheltering functions in the cold of winter when instead its winter beauty brings joy to those who delight in its snow covered limbs;" or, "And unlike the tree, you have words and a voice to express and communicate so much more."]*

**You notice the many characteristics of this tree that define it, and the many characteristics of you which define you, some that are discarded, some that are eternal, and some that are developing. There is much to learn from this tree. [Pause to give time for the internal thinking/feeling.]**

*[For many, the tree represents a positive parental or mentoring figure.]*

**After a while, you will be ready to continue your journey, to return to the path, taking with you the new knowledge, the feelings, and the sensations that you have experienced with this grand tree—all the knowledge, feelings, and**

**sensations that are useful to you—integrating this experience with each step that you take.**

*[Suggesting integration, which encourages meaning making, reflection, and awareness.]*

**Remembering that you may return to this tree at any time, to its soothing and wise presence, you now take leave of the tree. You return to your path, with each breath in, and discover yourself returning to the place where you started your journey. Again feeling the sure way in which mother earth comes to greet each footstep as you leave your fine imprint on the ground beneath your feet.**

**Mother earth, mother nature, the soles of one's feet (which can be heard as the souls), are archetypal images that carry both individual and societal meaning, subtly incorporating spirit into mind and body.**

*[At this point you proceed with suggestions for further realerting, and followed by a thorough discussion (exploration) of the client's experience during this guided hypnotic imagery.]*

## References

Ewin, D. (2009). *101 things I wish I'd known when I started using hypnosis*. Carmathen, Wales: Crown House.

## For Further Reading...

Anbar, R., & Linden, J. (2010). Understanding dissociation and insight in the treatment of shortness of breath with hypnosis: A case study. *American Journal of Clinical Hypnosis, 52,* 263-274.

Linden, J. (1984). Hypnosis as a therapeutic tool in the clinical setting, cystic fibrosis management update. In D. V. Schidlow (Ed.), *Proceedings of the 3rd (1984) Annual Regional Cystic Fibrosis Educational Retreat.*

Linden, J. (1995). When mind-body integrity is traumatized by problems with physical health: The woman's response. In G. Burrows & R. Stanley (Eds.), *Contemporary International Hypnosis*. New York, NY: Wiley.

Linden, J. (1996). Trauma prevention: Hypnoidal techniques with the chronically ill child. *Hypnos, 23,* 65-75.

Linden, J. (1997). On the art of hypnotherapy with women: Journeys to the birthplace of belief and other recipes for life. *Hypnos, 24,* 138-147.

Linden, J. (1999). Discussion of symposium enhancing healing: The contributions of hypnosis to women's health care. *American Journal of Clinical Hypnosis, 42,* 140-145.

Linden, J. (2001). Patient selection: Assessment and preparation, indications and contraindications. In G. Burrows, R. Stanley, & P. Bloom (Eds.), *International handbook of clinical hypnosis* (pp. 35-47). Chichester, UK: John Wiley & Sons.

Linden, J. (2002). The application of hypnosis to children and adolescents traumatized by war. In B. Peter, W. Bongartz, D. Revenstorf, & W. Butollo (Eds.), *Munich 2000, the 15th International Congress of Hypnosis, Hypnosis International Monographs Number 6* (pp. 21-29). Munich, Germany: MEG.

Linden, J. (2003). Playful metaphors. *American Journal of Clinical Hypnosis, 45,* 245-250.

Linden, J. (2003). Sandtray hypnosis. *Hypnos, 30,* 196-203.

Linden, J. (2004). Hypnosis: An integrative approach. *Psychological Hypnosis, 13,* 4-5.

Linden, J. (2004). Hypnotic identity—or what keeps us in the division? *Psychological Hypnosis, 13,* 20-21.

Linden, J. (2004). Making hypnotic interventions more powerful with a developmental perspective. *Psychological Hypnosis, 13,* 7-9.

Linden, J. (2005). Hypnosis in pain management or modifying the patient pain relationship. *Psychological Hypnosis, 14,* 14-17.

Linden, J., Bhardwaj, A., & Anbar, R. (2006). Hypnotically enhanced dreaming to achieve symptom reduction: A case study of 11 children and adolescents. *American Journal of Clinical Hypnosis, 48,* 279-289.

Linden, J. (2007). And this little piggy stayed home: Playful metaphors in treating childhood separation anxiety. In G. Burns (Ed.), *Healing with stories: Your casebook guide to effectively using therapeutic metaphors* (pp. 44-55). New York, NY: John Wiley and Sons.

Linden, J. (2007). Hypnosis with adolescents and developmental aspects of hypnosis with adults. In W. Wester & L. Sugarman (Eds.), *Therapeutic hypnosis with children and adolescents*. Williston, VT: Crown House.

Linden, J. (2007). Hypnosis in childhood trauma. In W. Wester & L. Sugarman (Eds.), *Therapeutic hypnosis with children and adolescents*. Williston, VT: Crown House.

Linden, J. (2009). Creativita consapevole: trance-formare I bambini con la psicoterapia [Creative integration of hypnosis into clinical psychotherapy with children]. In M. *L. Fasciana (Ed.), L'ipnosis con I bambini e gli adolescent* [*Hypnosis with children and adolescents*]. Milan, Italy: FrancoAngeli.

Linden, J. (2009). Identità di genere: Essere donna oggi [How we define our feminine selves: The kaleidoscopic view of gender identity]. In C. Casula (Ed.), *Le scarpe della principessa* [*The princess's shoes*]. Milan, Italy: FrancoAngeli/Le Comete.

Linden, J. (2011). Hypnosis and parents: Pattern interruptus. *American Journal of Clinical Hypnosis, 54,* 70-81.

Linden, J. (2011). La créativité attentive: Transe-former les enfants par la psychothérapie [Mindful Creativity: Trance-forming kids through psychotherapy]. *Hypnose & Thérapies Brèves, 21,* 18-37.

Linden, J. (2014). Hypnosis in childhood trauma. In W. Wester & L. Sugarman (Eds.), *Therapeutic hypnosis with children and adolescents* (2nd ed.). Williston, VT: Crown House.

Linden, J. (2014). Hypnosis with adolescents and developmental aspects of hypnosis with adults. In W. Wester & L. Sugarman (Eds.), *Therapeutic hypnosis with children and adolescents* (2nd ed.). Williston, VT: Crown House.

Linden, J. (2014). When and how to refer a patient to a mental healthcare provider. In R. Anbar (Ed.), *Functional symptoms in pediatric disease* (pp. 251-267). New York, NY: Springer.

Linden, J. (2015). Brain–gut bi-directional axis and hypnotic communication. (Guest Editorial). *American Journal of Clinical Hypnosis, 58,* 1-4.

# CHAPTER 4

# Conscious/Unconscious Dissociation Inductions

## Stephen R. Lankton

*Stephen R. Lankton is a licensed clinical social worker (LCSW) in Phoenix, Arizona. He is editor-in-chief of the* American Journal of Clinical Hypnosis *(since 2005) and a fellow and approved consultant of the American Society of Clinical Hypnosis. He began clinical practice in 1974 and has trained therapists worldwide since 1978. He has served as chair of the Arizona Board of Behavioral Health Examiners. He is a diplomate in clinical hypnosis (DAHB) and president emeritus of the American Hypnosis Board for Clinical Social Work.*

*His awards include "Lifetime Achievement Award for Outstanding Contribution to the Field of Psychotherapy," the "Irving Secter Award for the Advancement of Clinical Hypnosis," and "Lifetime Achievement Award for Contributions to the Field of Hypnosis and Hypnosis Education." He is the author and/or editor of 18 clinical books and dozens of professional articles and chapters. His work has been translated into six languages. He is an adjunct professor at Arizona State University, Graduate School of Social Work.*

* * *

To experience change, we have to change experience. Psychotherapy using hypnosis is the process of teaching people to change experience and produce more creative and adaptive living. The hypnotic induction, itself, is a complicated process of helping clients organize their experience and create a bridge from their current state of consciousness to one that is considered a therapeutic trance. Regardless of the criteria one may use to define therapeutic trance, the induction process remains much the same: stimuli created by the therapist (usually verbal) that has been formulated by the therapist and guided, to some degree, by the actions and behavior of the client. These stimuli, in turn, are translated into experience by the client who, in the process purposefully or unwittingly, communicates back to the therapist. As this entrainment continues, the therapeutic trance is elicited.

A creative and responsive therapist will carefully use this process to articulate and organize the conditions that are most salient for clients to develop their unique therapeutic trance. Induction uses various means of communication to revivify or evoke a set of necessary experiences from one or more states of consciousness. For instance, this set of experiences might include relaxing on the beach, a feeling of floating from a ride at Disneyland, the experience of visual and kinesthetic dissociation that one may have during scuba diving, and the sense of objectively examining something from a distance like solving a jigsaw puzzle, etc. I have explained this in greater detail in a states of consciousness (SoC) model of trance and induction published elsewhere (Lankton, 1985; Lankton, 2015). Some of the key features of the SoC process include: the therapist's use of stimuli which are personally meaningful to the client, noticing the client has acquired the experience being spoken about, and estimating which combination of experiences will most closely define a desirable trance state.

Among the factors that affect the induction process are the therapist's perceived prestige, the client's expectations and motivation, and communication variables of the induction language. So, there are some situations in which induction appears remarkably simple—this can happen when perceived prestige and motivation are high and the client/subject has previously learned the experience of trance. This chapter is not about such situations but rather discusses induction with clients who may have little or no expectations of success, may have low motivation, and do not attribute special prestige to the therapist—the clients who are sometimes labeled as "resistant."

**Premises**

I believe that each client requires a unique induction process, and usually each session requires a unique induction for the work in hypnosis to be maximally effective. The reason for this is the ever-changing experience of each client, which brings new concerns or new facets to old concerns. The name given to this approach is "naturalistic induction." In the first issue of the *American Journal of Clinical Hypnosis,* Milton H. Erickson (1958) defined and described the naturalistic techniques of hypnosis:

> The naturalistic approach to the problem of the induction of hypnotic trances—as opposed to formalized ritualistic procedures of trance induction—merits much more investigation, experimentation and study than have been accorded to date. By naturalistic approach is meant the acceptance of the situation

> encountered and the utilization of it, without endeavoring to restructure it psychologically. In so doing, the presenting behavior of the patient becomes a definite aid and an actual part in inducing a trance, rather than a possible hindrance. For lack of a more definite terminology, the method may be termed a naturalistic approach, in which an aspect of the principle of synergism is utilized. (p. 3)

Additional underlying concepts regarding my preferred type of induction should also be explained. The next concerns the manner in which people make or find meaning in communication. "Transderivational search" (TDS) (Lankton, 2003/1980, p. 193) is an unconscious search across possible meanings in order to locate a match (or the closest match) for received communication. During the search process (lasting milliseconds to many seconds), there is a heightened readiness for a specific meaningful referent and the experience associated with it. This duration, in the conscious mind, can be thought of as a creative precommitment to action or judgment (Perls, Hefferline, & Goodman, 1951). Throughout the TDS, the mind is keen on discovering a referent that will end the search and reduce the mental energy the search requires. Consequently, the listener will more willingly latch onto the meaning of communicational elements (words) for which he or she has previously attached meaning. In simpler terms, if the communication contains a good deal of ambiguity interspersed with the word "relax," the listener can resolve the search for the meaning of the ambiguousness by making meaning of the word "relax." Most indirect trance suggestions, as well as many direct suggestions, are ambiguous (e.g., using words or phrases such as "conscious," "unconscious," "sooner or later," "wonder," "learn," etc.) and sprinkled within and among them are words that refer to conditioned responses (e.g., "relax," "close your eyes," "feel comfort," etc.). It should be apparent, then, that a careful elaboration of ambiguity and evoked experiences can shape both induction and therapy within hypnosis.

The final concept involves the "conscious/unconscious dissociation" principle (Lankton & Lankton, 2008/1983). Erickson brought this concept to my attention when I first began contacting and then studying with him beginning in mid-1975. However, in 1939 he wrote, "...hypnosis may be induced by [he lists various procedures] that increases the degree of dissociation between consciousness and subconsciousness, thus establishing in effect but not in actuality a dissociated hypnotic personality" (Erickson, 2008, p. 12). This approach is represented in his selection of language represented throughout many of his published works. For instance:

> Now it really doesn't matter what your conscious mind does because it is your unconscious that will find new possibilities that your conscious mind is unaware of or may have forgotten...Yet your unconscious can work on them all by itself. And how will they be communicated to your conscious mind? (Erickson & Rossi, 1975, p. 153)

Sometimes, he even went so far as to emphasize each aspect with different voice tones: "I use one tone of voice to speak to the conscious mind and another to speak to the unconscious... you are establishing a duality" (Erickson &

Rossi, 1976, pp. 159-160). His rationale is that only in this way could the therapist "... secure an extensive dissociation" of the conscious from the unconscious and allow satisfactory access to, and use of, those parts for therapy or research (Erickson, 2008, p. 13).

### Case Example of Induction with Commentary

The following is a transcription from a trance about 16 minutes in length. The client was a 28-year-old man who made an outstanding number of negative self-related comments. He reported being depressed and hopeless and sought help only to make sure his 8-year-old son, of whom he had custody, was "not being too messed up" due to, according to him, him "being a loser." This transcript does not focus on the therapy, but rather trance induction. Nevertheless, it should be apparent that some therapy begins and is an essential part of the naturalistic induction process, particularly if the therapist is speaking the client's language and being relevant.

**Lankton: Well, let's talk about something you've done right, for a few minutes.**

*[Switching the topic from the "reality" of his faults to something positive about himself.]*

**Client: Okay.**

**Lankton: And, it comes to mind, as you're changing things in your life. I wonder, if you could say what's the most powerful experience you ever had in the stuff you've really done...**

*[Presupposing he is changing things.]*

**shall we say, "well?"**

*["Shall we say"—doesn't require an answer that others would endorse.]*

**You don't have to tell me, but, can you remember it for a second and then when you're there—tell me about it?**

*["Don't tell me... tell me" bypasses his reluctance to recall and then requests that he tell me after any anxiety to perform has been removed.]*

**Client: The only thing that I can, the first thing that always comes to my mind is my relationship with my son. He's a great, great kid. He's an incredible person.**

**Lankton: So you've given him a relationship quality that you're proud of.**

*[Labeled the experience as "proud" despite the client's not doing so.]*

**Client: Mm-hmm!**

*[Client accepts the "proud" label.]*

**Lankton: Then you must take a lot of comfort knowing you raised and taught him?**

*[Using that he raised him, I now introduce "comfort."]*

**Client: I do. I feel like, God, I did one thing really well. It makes me feel, um, you know... good or a little okay, I guess you'd say.**

*[Client accepts the experience of "comfort" also and adds "a little okay."]*

**Lankton: Uh-huh. You're smiling, you know? So, you feel confidence... pride... maybe some degree of satisfaction—and that brings you comfort. Would that be right?**

*[Shifting awareness to his bodily state—first the verifiable smiling, then introducing two other feelings that are linked to pride and comfort.]*

**Client: Yeah. I never really, I never, well, dwelled on it... or...**

*[Client is testing the situation. It is as if he is asking, "Is it really okay to feel those feelings?" This unspoken question is really an unconscious contract requesting permission to have and use them.]*

**Lankton: So this comfort you have is waiting for you to embrace it... enjoy it... savor it—let's do that now.**

*[Confirmation it is permissible to own those feelings.]*

**Hold on to it and close your eyes [pause].**

*[Asking for eye closure is an apparent permission to feel those feelings.]*

**I don't know if you know how to use it.**

*[The focus shifts from having the feelings to using them—thus setting up a therapy session that responds to his very shy request noted above.]*

**I wonder if you know how your unconscious can let it become more and more conscious? [pause].**

*[A conscious/unconscious dissociation is begun.]*

**And as it does, you may find that you either relax more and more to feel it... or that as you increasingly feel it you relax more and more.**

*[Relaxing and feeling—or—feeling and relaxing continues a conscious/unconscious dissociation experience.]*

**Client: [Takes a deep breath and exhales with a prolonged yawn.]**

*[This behavior represents the client's unconscious acceptance of the direction of the session.]*

**Lankton: Your yawn is a way of telling me your enjoyment of comfort and good feelings is long overdue. And we can make up for lost time if we can do hypnosis successfully for 25 minutes or so.**

*[Interpreting the yawn as a signal (the client can hardly deny it) to have the desired feelings he usually suppresses. The idea of using hypnosis is introduced (again, a naturalistic induction) for his own benefit and based on verifiable (to him) experience.]*

**Client: [Gently nods head, "yes," a few times.] I guess so.**

*[Client accepts the contract.]*

**Lankton: You should know that hypnosis is a state of heightened concentration where you, where you can turn your awareness to internal experiences [more slowly—speaking phrases in rhythm with the client's exhalation and inhalation].**

*[Explaining hypnosis so as to demystify it before proceeding.]*

**Sooner or later, with your internal experience, you can get a hold of and magnify your comfort, your confidence.**

*[Truism.]*

**And, why can't we take those feelings and have you project them into the future things that you haven't done and you want to do...**

*[Presupposition: They exist and we can take and project them into the future where you will need them.]*

**and do with ever increasing relaxation, comfort, and even confidence?**

*[Presupposition: Increasing relaxation.]*

**Your conscious mind may be surprised as to how you can trust your unconscious mind to do that. Your conscious mind may think of that interview you have on Friday while your unconscious attaches comfort and confidence to it... or your conscious mind may hold on to the comfort and confidence while you let your unconscious think of the places you want to feel this way [pause].**

*[Conscious/unconscious dissociation language ... (he appears comfortable with the terminology)... and continues... dissociation.]*

**And you might like to go deeper—become more deeply absorbed into those feelings and future opportunities.**

*[Focusing awareness on his depth of absorption... deepening.]*

**I wonder which of your eyes is more relaxed? Is the left corner of the right eye more relaxed than the right corner of your right eye? Or, is the right corner of your left eye more relaxed than the left corner of your left eye?**

*[Focusing awareness on his eyes to be sure he is focused on his feeling-experience... this is a bind of comparable alternatives.]*

**Each time you investigate that you will find that you become more relaxed than before. And as you wonder which is more relaxed you may decide the usual chatter in your mind is gone...**

*[Presupposition: Each time, you will.]*

**and you can go deeper into your experiences of relaxation, comfort, and confidence.**

*[Causal linking suggestion: Each time will cause you to go deeper into focusing awareness and returning to the feelings of comfort, etc.]*

**Lankton: [pause]. I would be surprised if you knew for sure which index finger would rise up to signal "yes" to questions I ask. Do you think you know which index finger will rise? [pause].**

*[Focusing awareness on his fingers and presupposing movement.]*

**I wonder if you know, yet? Are you very relaxed?**

*[Focusing on relaxation (and all that is now associated with it) to ensure he does not arouse from trance.]*

**Client: [left index finger rises].**

*[Ideomotor response.]*

**Lankton: Are you very, very relaxed and comfortable?**

*[Checking that this is a valid response.]*

**Client: [left index finger rises].**

*[Client confirms.]*

**Lankton: And now we know which finger will raise up. Now, if you tune me out don't worry about it, your unconscious is still listening and keeping you on target.**

*[Reinforcing, ratifying, and continuing the conscious/unconscious dissociation.]*

**So you can put your attention on other things.**

*[Open-ended suggestion, put attention on "other things."]*

**Such as thinking about that positive relationship.**

*[Focusing awareness.]*

**And so, specific aspects of it that might come to mind as I speak.**

*[Using the client's concern and words.]*

**I worked with a woman once in West Palm Beach who had, of all the things that had gone right or wrong in her life, just the best sense of her relationship with her child that she was able to rekindle by thinking about all the photos she kept in her wallet.**

*[Beginning an interspersed metaphor that reinforces and continues the conscious/unconscious dissociation by requiring the client to track two different lines of thought nearly simultaneously. The metaphor again matches the client's concerns and values.]*

**And let the relaxation move on down your hips and down your thighs and buttocks.**

*[Focusing awareness and helping make the pride, relaxation, confidence, etc., an entire-body experience.]*

**And as she sat there thinking about all the pictures she changed in her wallet over the last 9 years.**

*[Metaphor continues about visual experience... thus the metaphor vs. bodily comments greatly enhance the conscious/unconscious dissociation and since they are parallel in different sensory systems they will make the learning increasingly resistant to extinction (Bandura, 1969).]*

**And the places in the back of your mind that have to do with pride, we couldn't just say what those are. Bring**

**confidence and pride into the foreground, begin to bring tone to your cheeks and color your face.**

*[Presupposing there are more places of confidence. Focusing awareness on feeling and body experience again. All of this is congruent with the visual picture of the metaphor.]*

**And as she did that she flipped to another picture, and another one.**

*[Focusing awareness on a visual image of the self that is congruent with the desired feelings.]*

**So gradually and little by little let the feeling go down into your legs and feet.**

*[Focusing and moving the experience over more of the body.]*

**She began to have experiences of motherhood that you couldn't put words to. Sacrifices that she had made and feelings that she was able to mature. And identity that inadvertently she had formed for herself through the relationship that she'd never known she'd be able to share. That gave her a sense of pride, not only maturity—an identity that inadvertently she had formed for herself through the relationship.**

*[Continuing the conscious/ unconscious dissociation. The metaphor introduces thought about other accomplishments he has made (sacrifices, maturity) and the "conclusion" that this formed an identity—a positive identity (not the negative one he presented)—due to the feelings of pride and the accomplishments that were just visually imagined.]*

**Then notice as you have, your own experiences… and, how they give certain shape to the muscle tone in your cheeks and your lips, the corner of your eyes where a sense of**

**your own balance comes into the foreground and remains...**

*[Focusing attention back to his physical feelings and emotions (all congruent with the images and ideas of the metaphor).]*

**And the recognition that even though she had taken a great deal by learning that identity she hadn't taken away from her son at all, she had only given. And somehow there's no tax on receiving.**

*[Giving to his son also gained something for him and he did not need to feel reluctant to have earned it... there is no "tax on receiving" those sorts of feelings.]*

**Lankton: [pause]. It's all right to shift your awareness from time to time to let the joy that you feel, adjust your breathing and maybe even feeling your heart beating in your chest. So many people fail to take the time to associate their good feelings to their heart. Now they give lip service to it, but they don't really do it.**

*[Reframed the previous experience to now be "joy." Focusing awareness to associate joy to his heart.]*

**So, while you're feeling those feelings of pride and joy, being touched, there's the rhythm of your own heartbeat. Because that brings those feelings to your face and to your shoulders, to your legs, and to your abdomen. And that takes those hormones and those chemicals all over your body and increases your immune system functioning simply by taking the time...**

*[Continuing with direct attention on bodily states.]*

**to pay attention to your own joy and your own pride and confidence and associate it to your heart.**

*["Your own joy and your own pride" helps create a self-image (i.e., he can think of himself with pride and joy instead of only a loser).]*

**Lankton: [pause]. And you couldn't consciously know how you do that but sooner or later your conscious symbols of doing that create the unconscious experience so that new ideas can be formed in your mind.**

*[Continued conscious/unconscious dissociation suggestions.]*

**And one of those ideas can be your conscious efforts to watch yourself taking another step in your own personal growth.**

*[Continued creating a visual self-image.]*

**Picture yourself as you probably will look in the next few weeks and months. While you continue to hold that experience in your heart and your breathing. And you don't even need to know whether or not you're succeeding in any particular phase as long as you have those fleeting sensations of imagining and picturing that.**

*[Posthypnotic suggestions that he will see himself (parallel to the visual metaphor) taking new steps that will continue to be associated with pride, comfort, and confidence. These visuals have been associated with the feelings via both the metaphor and the coexistence of the conscious/unconscious pairing.]*

## Summary

In summary, this chapter illustrates how induction can be performed speaking the client's experiential language, creating "apparently" relevant ambiguity, and helping create an acceptance for unconscious resources using a conscious/unconscious dissociation. I have found that inductions, and in fact therapy, offered in this manner reaches a wider variety of clients, including those considered and readily labeled resistant. The interspersed, relevant, therapeutic work is integral to the naturalistic and conscious/unconscious approach of the induction. And, of course, additional work of therapy in hypnosis can and should follow the same premises. While this has been hinted in the transcript, details and examples of such therapy are beyond the scope of this chapter and can be found elsewhere (e.g., Lankton, & Lankton, 2008/1983; Lankton, 2004).

## References

Bandura, A. (1969). *Principles of behavior modification.* New York, NY: Holt, Rinehart & Winston.

Erickson, M. (1958). Naturalistic techniques of hypnosis. *American Journal of Clinical Hypnosis, 1,* 3-8.

Erickson, M. (2008). The application of hypnosis to psychiatry. In E. Rossi, R. Erickson-Klein, & K. Rossi (Eds.), *The collected works of Milton H. Erickson: Volume 2, basic hypnotic induction and suggestion* (pp. 9-20). Phoenix, AZ: The Milton H. Erickson Foundation Press.

Erickson, M., & Rossi, E. (1975). Varieties of double bind. *American Journal of Clinical Hypnosis, 17,* 143-157.

Erickson, M., & Rossi, E. (1976). Two-level communication and the microdynamics of trance and suggestion. *American Journal of Clinical Hypnosis, 18,* 153-171.

Lankton, S. (1985). A states of consciousness model of Ericksonian hypnosis. In S. Lankton, (Ed.), *Ericksonian monographs, number 1: Elements and dimensions of an Ericksonian approach* (pp. 26-41). New York, NY: Brunner/Mazel.

Lankton, S. (2003). *Practical magic: A translation of basic neuro-linguistic programming into clinical psychotherapy.* Williston, VT: Crown House. (Original work published 1980)

Lankton, S. (2004). *Assembling Ericksonian therapy: The collected papers of Stephen Lankton*. Phoenix, AZ: Zeig-Tucker.

Lankton, S. (2015). Editorial: A SoC model of hypnosis and induction. *American Journal of Clinical Hypnosis, 57*, 367-377.

Lankton, S., & Lankton, C. (2008). *The answer within: A clinical framework of Ericksonian hypnotherapy*. New York: Brunner/Mazel. (Original work published 1983)

Perls, F., Hefferline, R., & Goodman, P. (1951). *Gestalt therapy: Excitement and growth in the human personality*. New York, NY: Delta.

**For Further Reading…**

Lankton, S. (2008). *Tools of intention: Strategies that inspire change*. Williston, VT: Crown House.

Lankton, S. (2009). Using metaphor with clients. In A. Roberts (Ed.), *Social workers' desk reference* (2nd ed., pp. 578-587). New York, NY: Oxford University Press.

Lankton, S. (2010). A basic footprint of Milton H. Erickson's process of change. In E. L. Rossi, R. Erickson-Klein, & K. L. Rossi (Eds.). *The collected works of Milton H. Erickson: Classical hypnotic phenomena* (Part 2, Vol. 6, pp. 345-357). Phoenix, AZ: Milton H. Erickson Foundation Press.

Lankton, S. (2010). Ericksonian approaches to hypnosis and therapy. In D. Barrett (Ed.) *Hypnosis and hypnotherapy (Vol. 2): Applications in psychotherapy and medicine* (pp. 1-48). Santa Barbara, CA: Praeger.

Lankton, S. (2010). Using hypnosis in Redecision Therapy. *Transactional Analysis Journal, 40*, 99-107.

Lankton, S. (2015). Hypnosis and therapy for a case of vomiting, nausea, and pain. *American Journal of Clinical Hypnosis, 58*, 63-80.

Lankton, S. (2015). Hypnotherapy. In E. S. Neukrug (Ed.), *The SAGE Encyclopedia of theory in counseling and psychotherapy* (pp. 524-528). Thousand Oaks, CA: Sage Publications.

Lankton, S. (2015). Using metaphor with clients. In K. Corcoran and A. Roberts (Eds.), *Social workers' desk reference* (3rd ed., pp. 629-639). New York, NY: Oxford University Press.

Lankton, S. (2016). Conscious/unconscious dissociation induction: Increasing hypnotic performance with resistant clients. *American Journal of Clinical Hypnosis, 59,* 175-185.

Lankton, S., & Matthews, W. (2010). An Ericksonian model of clinical hypnosis. In S. Lynn, J. Rhue, & I. Kirsch (Eds.) *Handbook of clinical hypnosis* (2nd ed., pp. 209-238). Washington, DC: American Psychological Association Press.

# CHAPTER 5

# Rapid and Instantaneous Hypnosis Inductions

**Gabor Filo**

*Gabor Filo has been an ardent proponent of dental hypnosis since his liberation from dental school. He has been spelunking in musty libraries and arcane tomes, studying and practicing hypnosis for over 40 years. In his general dental practice, he utilizes hypnosis with predominantly fearful, anxious, and phobic patients. In caring for all his patients, he utilizes many of the phenomena associated with hypnosis such as anesthesia, time distortion, and hemostasis as needed and appropriate.*

*Due to the nature and time constraints of dental practice, he has become increasingly interested in rapid and instantaneous hypnotic inductions. To that end he has produced a DVD which was recently published by Crown House Publishers.*

*Dr. Filo is a Diplomate of the American Board of Hypnosis in Dentistry, a Fellow of the American Society of Clinical Hypnosis (ASCH), and an honorary member of the Canadian Society of Clinical Hypnosis Ontario Division. For many years, he has served as faculty for the ASCH and has presented internationally on the subject to Allied Health Care professionals and proselytized at numerous North American dental conferences. Many professional hypnosis and dental organizations have also benefited from his involvement at the organizational level.*

* * *

Many of us work in chaotic, cacophonous, fast paced, high stress, overhead rich, clinical contexts in which the luxury of protracted inductions is precluded. Not only do the contextual demand characteristics hinder our efforts, but the anxious, distressed patients with their kith and kin are expecting rapid definitive interventions. To reframe: no one wants to spend time at the boarding gate; they want to be airborne on their way to their destination. Thus, knowledge of rapid and instantaneous inductions is crucial.

In many clinical situations, our role is not to induce a trance but to recognize the one that the patient may already have when he or she walks into the office. This is Ericksonian utilization at its most demanding. The hypnoidal states will usually be sympathetic nervous system driven rather than the desired parasympathetic mediated. Our assignment, then, is to help the patient shift to a neutral or parasympathetic modulated hypnotic state.

Your paradigm of hypnosis in such moments may be either permissive or authoritarian (in acute situations authoritarian is recommended), direct or indirect, maternal or paternal, overt or covert. The ethics of a covert induction are left to the individual practitioner's conscience to wrestle into acceptable submission.

The patient must have a need, must believe that you have the solution for that need, and they must be willing to participate; that is, he or she must be motivated. When the situation is dire—a life-threatening trauma for example—it is possible to dispense with preinduction preparation altogether. The rarely used *shock* induction, for example, is feasible without the listed patient characteristics being present.

Stage and street hypnotists are the usual exponents of rapid inductions today (McGill, 1996). Of course, the dangers of and adverse events associated with hypnosis when used as entertainment by lay people or stage hypnotists are well known (e.g., Gruzelier, 2000). This is the reason that such use of hypnosis is against the law in some countries, and most if not all professional hypnosis societies strongly advocate that hypnosis should not be used as entertainment. Still, stage and street hypnotists have a great deal of experience in the development and application of rapid hypnotic inductions. They offer much to be learned and many hands-on clinical contexts have parallels to the stage setting. Shakespeare was prescient in stating that "All the world's a stage." A worthwhile eye-opening exercise is an exploration of your daily therapeutic encounters in theatrical terms.

A stage performance works because the following are present. A volunteer subject will be exposed to peer pressure from the other audience members. There will be a heightened sense of expectation from one and all. This is of course masterfully generated by the performer. Physiologically the volunteer subjects will experience an epinephrine surge, an increase in blood pressure that will lead to a narrowing of focus and heightened suggestibility. Once the hypnotist grants them permission to relax into the wondrous state of hypnosis, a fugue, they readily comply. They are *relieved* of personal responsibility for their actions; mitigate their discomfort-causing sympathetic symptoms and calmly escape the vigilance of the audience. The act of being observed also tends to make people more compliant to suggestions and directives.

One of the most important features of a successful performance on stage or in the clinic is the confidence of the hypnotist. Shaw talks about the clinician's prestige; that is, their skill and reputation. The greater their reputation, the less their need for demonstrated skill; conversely, the less their reputation is developed, the more the need for skill. Another way of phrasing this is to "fake it, 'till you make it"!

**The Components of a Rapid Induction**

1. Setting the stage by creating expectation utilizing what the client or patient brings or acknowledging the trance state that he or she is already in. This prepares your client for the induction. Stage performers have an advantage over the clinician with respect to this component.
2. Induction. The Rapid Induction technique that you use will be tailored to the specific circumstances and needs of the patient. These needs may be obvious or may need to be inferred.
3. Deepening or intensification can be accomplished using your preferred method—Dave Elman states that once there is an initiated trance, any suggestion thereafter deepens the state (Elman, 1964). I have found this to be true.
4. Intervention. The intervention suggestion will address the patient's needs or, on stage, it will be the act the volunteers are put through to entertain.
5. Exduction, reorientation or dehypnotization by whatever means is most conducive to the context. This may be counting out, permissive reorientation, physical cue, or if appropriate additional

posthypnotic suggestions, such as suggestions for a restful sleep.

6. Post frame or debriefing suggestions after realerting will give your client conscious reinforcement in the waking state to aid them in fully benefiting from their experience (Stoiber, 2013).

## The Nature of Rapid Inductions

Classically, rapid inductions on the stage used physical methods that relied upon the startle or shock effect to induce a surge of epinephrine. The sudden flight, fright, and *freeze* response offers the moment for deepening suggestions. Both verbal (usually an emphatic "sleep" command) and physical reinforcement of heaviness and expertly appropriately applied pressure intensify the trance. Derivatives employ variations on fascination—waving fingers in front of the subject's eyes or gazing fixedly into his or her eyes, before the startling command. These types of induction have very little clinical utility for obvious reasons. They tend now to be the domain of street hypnotists. However, having them in the toolbox is not a bad thing. Even a wrench can be used as a hammer.

Other forms are more conducive to clinical practice. Dave Elman's full induction (which will be parsed below) takes less than 3 minutes from start to Esdaile coma (Elman, 1964). It is a combination of verbal suggestions and incorporates some physical touch. It can be either authoritarian or permissive in delivery depending on the needs of the patient, the context, and your personal style. This induction translates well into virtually any setting and context.

Some inductions can be done nonverbally using mesmeric passes or verbally with equal success. The mechanisms and paradigms of operation can be debated until research delivers something of a definitive explanation. However, in a hands-on clinical context, knowledge about the mechanisms of action are a luxury that can be pragmatically ignored in favor of results.

## Favorite Inductions with Commentaries

The following four inductions cover the spectrum of models and theories of hypnosis. I will let the reader speculate about the mechanisms at play. They are presented in outline form, accompanied with a parsing explanation, as everyone must make an induction's patter their own to be successful. Linchpin phrases and expressions are indicated in italics and should be used verbatim.

### Elman's Method

Dave Elman wrote one of the seminal books on hypnosis, *Hypnotherapy,* in which he systematically builds up to this induction (Elman, 1964). Each section can be used independently. Together they are a powerful whole that can induce anesthesia in no more than 3 minutes. I speak from experience having used this in the backcountry under primitive conditions with patients suffering from extensive second degree burns to dislocated shoulders. The delivery can be very authoritarian, as Elman used it, to permissive depending on your style and the circumstances.

**Clinician: Take a deep breath and close your eyes.**

*[Elman would always instruct the patient to close their eyes only when told to do so. He would find a reason to challenge them to do it again only on command. The badgering establishes a nidus of control which can be dispensed with today.]*

**Now *pretend* that your eyelids are so heavy that you are not able to open your eyes. *They just won't work!***

*[This is the beginning of eyelid catalepsy using imaginal processes to fatigue the weakest muscle. The key phrase is "they just won't work."]*

**When you are certain that you will be unable to open your eyes, go ahead and "*try.*" That's right, they just won't work. And at the same time, as you try, you feel even more relaxed. Very good. Now you can relax the eyes and open your eyelids.**

**And now, the eyelids are becoming heavy again, so heavy they that you cannot open them. That's right. And again, when you know that you will be unable to open your eyes, go ahead and "*try.*" That's right, they won't work. And you feel *even more* relaxed. The relaxation and comfort doubles. Now, again, you can relax the eyes and open your eyelids.**

*[Repeat three times in fairly rapid succession. Each time have relaxation doubling or trebling; mention may be made of the increased comfort. The fractionation enhances depth and intensifies the experience.]*

**And now one more time. The eyelids are becoming heavy again, so heavy they that you cannot open them. That's right. And when you again know that you will be unable to open your eyes, go ahead and "*try.*" They won't work. And you feel *even more* relaxed. The relaxation and comfort doubles again. Now, again, you can relax the eyes and open your eyelids. Go ahead and try. Even *more* relaxed, *more* comfortable.**

**Last time, let eyes remain closed and we will move on...**

*[Test degree of physical relaxation by lifting the patient's hand a few inches and dropping it. The hand should fall into lap without effort. If not, spend more time on the deepening.]*

**Now, count out loud backwards from 100. With each number, you can double the relaxation and comfort.**

*[Further deepening preparing to set up amnesia.]*

**And at the number 98, you can forget the numbers.**

*[Eliciting amnesia further intensifies trance. If they have not forgotten the numbers, then have them "turn off the lights" or "clean them off a blackboard."]*

**I am now going to stroke the back of your hand three times.**

*[Pick the hand closest to you for ease. Stroke it three times.]*

**With each stroke, your relaxation doubles. And you will notice a change in the feeling of the hand. The sensation will become more profound with each stroke.**

**You may start to feel feelings of numbness, like making a snowball with your bare hand.**

*[Any metaphor including injection of local anesthetic may work if there are no contraindications, e.g., needle phobic or allergy to local (Guttman, 2013).]*

**Now, remain just as you are, and open your eyes. And compare both of your hands.**

*[Eliciting eyes open trance. The exact phrase is important to have them stay in trance. And then trance and anesthesia are ratified as they look at the anesthetized hand. In the old days, a needle would be inserted into the back of the hand with the glove anesthesia; today a pinch is used to ratify the anesthesia.]*

**Now, go ahead and close your eyes again.**

*[At this point, the therapy can begin (if psychological) or moving onwards to further physiological control.]*

**Having experienced physical relaxation, do you wish to experience mental relaxation as well?**

*[Permission and suggestion of deeper state possibility—eliciting anticipation and participation.]*

**Okay, we can now go together on an elevator, going down three floors to the basement of relaxation.**

*[Deepening. Key word is basement as a metaphor for depth. Arriving at Esdaile Coma or somnambular or plenary trance.]*

**And now that we are there, the doors open into a "safe room."**

**Very good. And now, you can count with me to come back. I will count to 10, and with each number, you will feel more and more alert...**

*[Counting out is good to ensure full alerting.]*

### Filo's Cataleptic Arm

The arm catalepsy induction is a classic induction. The method as I use it is an amalgam of its variations and other components I have culled from Hartland (Mahteson & Grehan, 1979), Erickson, Mesmer, and neurolinguistic programming (Filo, 2012). It can be done verbally or nonverbally. The nonverbal form requires some practice in acquiring the subtleties of recognizing when arm catalepsy has actually occurred.

**Clinician: Do you have a favorite TV program? I don't want to know what it is; you don't have to tell me. You may close or leave your eyes open...**

*[Permissive elicitation of cooperation. If the patient does not have a favorite TV program, then invite them to choose one or imagine one. For the nonvisual, audio favorites can be used. For inward focus we want to utilize the full sensorium starting with the patient's preferred modality, i.e., visual, kinesthetic, or auditory.]*

**[Take the patient's non-dominant arm and have him or her hold it out in front, pretending it is a TV antenna—the more rigid the antenna, the better the reception.]**

*[Works with the dominant hand also, but why not use their non-dominant hemisphere for maximum affect and effect? Sets up arm catalepsy.]*

**Imagine sitting in your favorite TV-watching chair, turn on the TV, adjust the volume, see the screen and feel the chair. If you like... popcorn or other snacks, taste them and smell them.**

*[Suggestion to go inwards with absorption in TV program through the full use of the sensorium.]*

**The more rigid the antenna, the better the reception.**

*[Deepening.]*

**Now while watching your program, let your hand from the wrist to the fingertips become numb as though playing with a snowball...**

*[Induce glove anesthesia (GA) on outstretched cataleptic hand.]*

**Remain just the way you are and compare hands.**

**[The pinch test can be done; then transfer glove anesthesia to needed region].**

*[Eyes open trance with glove anesthesia. Trance validation with dissociation. Recommend ideomotor confirmation of transferred anesthesia before intervention. Realert with whatever method is appropriate, with or without posthypnotic suggestions.]*

**Barrett's Instant Meditation**

Rick Barrett is a Tai Chi practitioner who has created a bridge between the ancient martial art and Western science. In his revealing book (Barrett, 2006), he outlines a form of instant meditation that is bottom up. That is, he uses the body to engender a cessation in the chatter of the "monkey mind" (conscious mind). The approach is simple, yet versatile. I have used it with patients that have trust issues; those that do not wish to close their eyes or complain of not being able to visualize. Your creativity is the only limiting factor to its utility. It can be used to help with anything from stress management to anesthesia.

**Clinician: Stand or sit comfortably. Take a deep breath, hold it, and let it out slowly while relaxing.**

*[My usual introduction to most inductions.]*

**Place your hands on your thighs [table, etc.] and slightly raise your index fingers with no more energy than flicking on a light switch.**

*[Positioning the hands such that the index fingers are notably different from the other fingers.]*

**Focus on the physical sensations in the fingers...**

*[Directing the attention to observable physical sensations... a narrowing of focus with an internal trajectory.]*

**The circulation, the ligament stretch, the muscles, the air around them...**

**When the only sensations you are aware of are those of the index fingers..., move your awareness past the finger tips...**

*[A dissociation.]*

**You may notice that all of your racing thoughts... the mental chatter ... has ceased...**

*[Asking for a meta-awareness about the stillness of the mind. A further dissociation.]*

**If you notice intruding thoughts... relax, take another breath ... and refocus on your index fingers... repeat this several times... and notice how you are getting better at controlling the chatter...**

*[In meditative practice, this is the return to the thought object for refocusing or in hypnotic methods, the beginnings of a series of fractionations.]*

**Let this experience become more... and more... profound...**

*[Further intensification which can be followed by therapeutic or goal directed suggestions.]*

**Return to the present feeling refreshed and relaxed, ready to continue your day.**

*[Realerting. This is my usual patter followed by a debriefing to ensure full return to awareness.]*

**The Golden Moment Method**

In my use of this truly elegant induction, the expressions *golden moment* and *perfect moment* are used interchangeably.

As all inductions, it can be modified to the needs of the moment and in my experience works best in a permissive manner.

**Clinician: Take a deep breath and relax as you let it out...**

*[The subject may stand or sit. Hold your fingers in front of their face above eye level... an eye fixation.]*

**Think of a moment in your life that you consider a golden moment ... a perfect moment.**

*[Asking for an inward focus—reification of a memory. If they do not have one, ask them to imagine one.]*

**A moment... that you wish would have lasted forever...**

*[A temporal distortion.]*

**Go [back] there now...**

*[If sitting in a dental chair, have the chair concurrently move backwards into a prone position as you say this. A regression.]*

**Be there fully and see the sights... hear the sounds... feel the sensations... and smell the aromas of that perfect moment...**

*[Deepening by involving the full sensorium. Continue deepening or Intensification using most appropriate means.]*

*[Move to the therapeutic suggestions as needed, then realert by the most appropriate method when done with or without posthypnotic suggestions. Ensure full realerting.]*

Rapid inductions have been discussed as a separate unique entity or class of inductions. In reality, one should be aware that almost all hypnotic inductions can be rapid ones if the situation and its circumstances permit. This is the artistry of hypnosis, quite separate from its applications and scientific underpinnings.

## References

Barrett, R. (2006). *Taijiquan through the western gate.* Berkeley, CA: Blue Snake Books/Frog.

Edmonston, W. E., Jr. (1986). *The induction of hypnosis.* New York, NY: John Wiley & Sons.

Elman, D. (1964). *Hypnotherapy.* Glendale, CA: Westwood.

Filo, G. (Director). (2012). *Rapid hypnotic inductions demonstrations and applications* [Motion Picture]. Crown House.

Guttman, K. A. (2013). An unanticipated allergic reaction to a hypnotic suggestion for anesthesia: A brief communication and commentary. *American Journal of Clinical Hypnosis, 61,* 336-341.

Gruzelier, J. (2000). Unwanted effects of hypnosis: A review of the evidence and its implications. *Contemporary Hypnosis, 17,* 163-193.

Matheson, G., & Grehan, J. F. (1979). A rapid induction technique. *American Journal of Clinical Hypnosis, 21,* 297-299.

McGill, O. (1996). *The new encyclopedia of stage hypnotism.* Underwood St. Clears, Carmarthen, Wales: Anglo American Book Company.

Shaw, S. I. (1958). *Clinical applications of hypnosis in dentistry.* Philadelphia, PA: W. B. Saunders.

Stoiber, O. (2013). Rapid inductions: Conference notes (English) [Web log post]. Retrieved from https://www.hypnovita.de/blog/hypnoselernen/rapid-inductions-conference-notes-english

# CHAPTER 6

## The Induction of Eyes-Open Alert Waking Hypnosis

**David M. Wark**

*David Wark earned his bachelor's degree in Psychology at Pomona College, '56. He received a Ford Foundation Behavioral Science Fellowship at the University of Minnesota, where he completed his doctorate in 1961. After 2 years in the United States Army Medical Service Corps, during which time he helped found the National Society of Programmed Instruction, he returned to the University of Minnesota as staff in the Student Counseling Service and the Department of Psychology, developing, validating, and publishing strategies for attention, self-control, and efficient learning. In 1980, he began training in hypnosis, which he integrated into his practice.*

*He has served on the boards of the American Society of Clinical Hypnosis, the Society of Clinical and Experimental Hypnosis, the International Society of Hypnosis, and the National Pediatric Hypnosis Training Institute. He was the president of the Minnesota Society of Clinical Hypnosis for 1995-97 and of the American Society of Clinical Hypnosis for 2008-09. He is a diplomate and past president of the American Board of Psychological Hypnosis.*

*He has published 2 books and 80 articles and chapters on study skills, reading, hypnosis, and hypnosis training and is an internationally recognized leader in the use of alert eyes-open and active hypnosis.*

*Dr. Wark has traveled and taught hypnosis to professionals in America, Europe, and Asia. He is an emeritus professor of psychology, and maintains an active clinical practice in St. Paul, MN.*

* * *

My idea of eyes-open induction was inspired by two extraordinary psychologists that I met at an International Hypnosis Society meeting. At that time, I was on staff at the Student Counseling Service, University of Minnesota. Much of my work was with clients who were good students but were so anxious they did quite poorly on their exams. Traditional hypnotic treatment was working pretty well. But at the meeting, Lars-Erick Unestahl, who used hypnosis when he coached the Swedish Olympic gymnastics team (Unestahl, 1983), said something that fundamentally changed my thinking. He told me good athletes often had an experience when "the event runs them." I asked Lars-Eric for some ideas about how I could train students so that the "book reads them." He thought that was a good idea and encouraged me to explore this further.

That same day, in another workshop, I learned from Éva Bányai about active alert hypnosis. She was a professor of psychology in Hungary, convinced that hypnosis was not sleep. At that time in Hungary's history, Russian psychology dominated, and Pavlov taught that hypnosis was a form of sleep. Éva arranged to leave Hungary and work with Ernest Hilgard at Stanford. Together they developed an induction technique that involved subjects riding a stationary bicycle under load (Bányai & Hilgard, 1976). They found that in the same subjects, traditional and active hypnosis correlated very strongly ($r = .77$), and therefore it was nonsense to call hypnosis sleep. So, at that meeting I got two new ideas; eyes-open and active hypnosis that I could use back in Minnesota.

In order for hypnosis to be useful to my students, when they were in classrooms listening, writing notes, reading text, and answering questions, they needed a technique that involved open eyes. Lars-Eric and Éva taught me that it was possible to achieve hypnotic effects with an eyes-open induction. But my students needed an induction that they could do anywhere, without looking strange, and without a bicycle. I developed a focusing and breathing technique and published an article (Wark, 1989) as proof of concept.

Over the years, there have been alternative techniques for inducing eyes-open hypnosis (Alarcon, Capafons, Bayot, & Cardeña, 1999; Capafons, 1998; Cardeña, Alarcon, Capafons, & Bayot, 1998). There are numerous reports of alert hypnosis clinical applications in diverse fields: medicine, mental health, athletics, artistic performance, and education. (For further reading, see a partial list below.)

The applications of alert hypnosis vary widely. However, one finding seems to be common to many investigations. In a review of eight reports comparing alert and traditional inductions, subjects in alert hypnosis say they have a greater sense of participation (Wark, 1998). I take that to mean that with alert hypnosis, the user has a greater sense of personal involvement and control.

Over time, my ideas evolved. I thought of induction as eyes-open focus, using repeated cycles of increasing mental attention and decreasing physical tension. I used principles of repeated, spaced practice, following the guidelines for a spiral curriculum (Wark & Kohen, 2002). My idea was to develop an induction that used repetition, small steps progressing toward the ultimate goal, and the opportunity for the subject to process and report their own continuing observations of change. That planned sequence of activities culminated in alert, eyes-open hypnosis.

For this chapter, I think of an alert induction as involving seven specific, teachable skills. My examples and comments in the transcript and commentary below will focus on adolescent or adult students using the process to achieve a better academic outcome. The same principles apply to any area of clinical practice. Feel free to replace the word "students" with "clients," "patients," or "trainee." Read the comments below so that you will have some idea of the reasoning behind the script. Of course, modify to make it congruent with your approach.

### Skill 1: Define a goal suggestion to be used in hypnosis

As the first step toward hypnosis, take the time necessary to help your students specify a relevant personal goal statement. It should not be so broad as to be unmeasurable, nor so narrow to be irrelevant. Your job is to guide their progress in generating suggestions that seem appropriate, observable, and achievable. The endpoint is for them to articulate personal outcomes to be used as a hypnotic suggestion. Finally, tell the students to "Store it in your memory, in the back of your mind, so you can get it later."

### Skill 2: Do warm up exercises, to move mind and body further into hypnosis

As part of the induction, guide the students to notice and report, as they alternately inhale and exhale, tense and relax, how their bodies move. The first warm up exercise (see the transcript) is designed to practice a simple task: inhale and exhale, rhythmically. The desired result of the body-oriented exercise is that the students pay attention to what is going on inside their bodies and reduce awareness of the external environment. The second exercise is to practice inhibiting some particular thought. Specifically, you ask the students to imagine a leaf floating on a stream and then to stop the picture and fade the scene.

### Skill 3: Increase focus on a target, while tensing and relaxing

Once the students have the idea of the up and down, rhythmic, cyclic aspect of breathing, you can model techniques to increase hypnosis. Give students the task of watching, listening, and reporting what they hear and see you do. Offer yourself as their point of focus. Use the language in the script, or your own variation, to talk yourself through the induction. Speak your internal instructions aloud. Tell yourself (in the 1st first person, modeling for your students) "I look around and find a spot that holds my attention. Then I inhale and hold my breath – increase and keep my attention focused on the spot – breathe out and relax – but keep my attention on the spot." Repeat this for several cycles, each time increasing or "levering" up and holding your attention on the spot, and lowering your general level of physical tension. Stop, blink your eyes, and shake your arms, to alert out of hypnosis.

Ask the students what they saw and heard. Repeat the modeling until they are able, on their own, to notice and speak about the rhythmic, levering up, tensing and relaxing of your body, your rapt, unwavering and increasing visual attention to a spot, and whatever qualities they heard in your voice. Essentially, they are pacing you to learn the steps in the process.

After your modeling, ask the students to carry out Skill 3 on their own. Prompt them through several cycles, finding a spot for focus; inhaling; increasing attention; holding attention; exhaling at their preferred pace; and report their experience. Have them repeat the process until they mention that when they focus on the spot, the surroundings seem to change, to move, to fade, or even disappear completely. That perceptual change is a marker that they are moving into hypnosis.

### Skill 4: Deepen the experience of alert hypnosis

Somewhere in the process, either before or during the induction, train your students to use a simple 10-point analog scale for depth of focus, using the script in the comment section. The scale is modified from Tart (1970). Students are asked to repeat the levering cycle a few times, ask themselves what number indicates the depth of their hypnosis, and then continue focusing. With each exhalation, they are to whisper to themselves the word "deeper." After six or seven more cycles, ask them to report the number that indicates their depth.

There are two useful indicators of depth. One is a reported increase, for example from 2 to 5, indicating deeper focus. The other is a report in which the students say the target is in some way "different." The spot may appear bigger, the surroundings may fade, there may be a report of movement, or some other kind of visual surprise such as a halo around the spot. All of these are markers of visually focused attention, modified perception, and increased hypnotic depth.

**Skill 5: Recall and experience the goal suggestion**

At this point, when your students have achieved a satisfactory deep level, ask that they stay in hypnosis and recall the goal they had set up and placed in memory. See the transcript for suggestions.

**Skill 6: Carry out the goal suggestion, while in hypnosis**

If the situation allows, ask the students to carry out the goal in your presence. For example, if the goal is to do a reading assignment excellently, give the student a text to read while in alert hypnosis. You can ask questions about the passage, and have the student answer, still in alert hypnosis. Finally, alert the student back to a non-hypnotized state, to process the experience with you.

Here is an example of a goal suggestion for reading:

> I know reading involves the connections between words. I will focus on the page, on the paper, and on each word. I will notice the ideas that flow up from each sentence, recalling what I know that is associated with what I read now. I will let the words I read remind me of what I already know. As I'm reading, if any negative unwanted thoughts appear, I will say "No" and go back to the words. I will review and file that I am reading, so that I can remember it later.

For more examples of educationally appropriate suggestions for alert hypnosis (see Wark, 1990).

### Skill 7: Evaluate the experience and plan the next induction

After the hypnotic work, fully alert the students and ask them to evaluate their total experience. They should be able to tell you they: (1) articulated a goal as a suggestion; (2) entered and deepened hypnosis; (3) imagined themselves fully implementing the goal, and, if practical; (4) actually carried it out while in hypnosis. Ask them what worked well and what needs to be changed.

Do final coaching to ameliorate any problems or disappointments with the process. Help them recall and emphasize any successes, even if momentary and fleeting. Depending on their reaction, you might initiate their search for a safe, undisturbed place to practice. Another change may involve planning more time for practice. Perhaps present some alternatives for going deeper into hypnosis; taking longer and slower breaths, imagine floating on a cloud, drifting on a river if they are comfortable swimming, walking in a garden, or some other safe imagery—all those are good ways to increase hypnotic depth. Remind the students of other times when they developed an important skill, after several practice sessions.

### Induction Example with Commentary

*Skill 1: Create a personal goal*

**Clinician: So that you can proceed, please visualize a personal goal or intention for yourself; something you would like to do using alert self-hypnosis. Create and reach for a goal that would make you feel good, strong, happy! Your goal may involve something about your academic training, such as looking more alertly at the text when you read, or reciting and recalling right after you**

**finish an exercise, or creating a feeling of accomplishment with your work.**

*[This example is for a student using alert hypnosis to improve schoolwork. However, the same skills apply to hypnosis applications for mental health, medical procedures, habit control, social interaction, athletics, performance, etc. Your job is to help the student make appropriate suggestions that are concrete and specific. The objective is that the student generates and states personally meaningful outcomes. For some students, this may take more time than actually teaching hypnosis.]*

**After you have identified the experience and the environment for that goal, before you start focusing, write it down, and then store the memory in your mind for use later.**

*[Setting up a goal is part of the process of alert hypnosis. The student focuses on achievement and positive outcome. Guide the student to clarify a positive measurable and reasonable goal.]*

***Skill 2: Warm-up for the body and mind***

**Now you can do some warm-up exercises to get your body and mind ready for hypnosis. The first exercise is for your body.**

*[The warm-up is designed to prompt the student to say something like: "When I breathe in, my shoulders go up; when I exhale they go down." In this commentary there are some cues to guide your presentation. A short horizontal line, called an en dash (–) is a signal to pace your voice with the inhale – exhale pattern of a student's breathing. When working in a group, it may be appropriate to pace one student, and notice how the rest follow.]*

**Lift your head up toward the ceiling. Take a deep breath – hold it – exhale – and relax. What happens?**

**Repeat the inhale – hold it – exhale cycle until the student recognizes and reports sensations of moving up and coming down.**

**Now, press your legs down against the floor – take a deep breath – hold it – exhale – and relax.**

**What happens now?**

*[Again, the warm-up is designed to emphasize the inhale – tense up – hold it – exhale – relax down bodily motion. Repeat until the student reports body movement.]*

**Now, using your whole body – lift and press down at the same time – inhale – hold your breath – exhale – and relax. What happens?**

*[Repeat, if necessary, until the student is able to describe the physical sensations of the cycle: inhale – increase attention – hold it – exhale – and relax.]*

**Now, here is a warm-up for your mind, with your eyes open.**

**Imagine you are walking through a lovely forest. You can see the beautiful trees – smell the natural fragrance in the air – hear the sounds of nature all around you.**

*[This is an alert induction. Some students may want to close their eyes. It is probably better to discourage that. You want to establish the idea that their eyes can be open when they are in hypnosis.]*

**You come to a small flowing stream. You stand on the bank – watching the water flow. Looking upstream – you**

**see an interesting leaf floating on the water – drifting slowly down toward you.**

**When the leaf is in front of you, say "Stop." Hold the picture – looking closely at the leaf – notice the shape – notice the size – allow the rest of the world to disappear – slowly – slowly. You can increase your ability to concentrate and focus.**

*[Pace and lead as necessary. This is an exercise in inhibiting or stopping thought. Later, during alert hypnosis, the same techniques will be used to stop or inhibit distractions, and stay focused on a target.]*

**Now, blink your eyes two or three times, shake your arms, and come out of hypnosis.**

**What happened?**

*[Alert the student out of hypnosis and process the experience. The goal is for the student to say that they can stop, or inhibit an image. If not, repeat the exercise, with appropriate modifications, until you both are satisfied.]*

***Skill 3: Focus***

**Now I'm going to show you how to use the warm-up to get into alert hypnosis.**

**I'll do that by going into alert hypnosis myself, the way I usually do it. But I will talk out loud so that you can hear me. Your job is just to watch and listen, and then we will talk.**

*[Model the induction for the student. Talk through the process of picking a spot to look at, taking a deep breath, and lifting your head and shoulders toward the ceiling, holding your breath, focusing on the spot, exhaling and relaxing. Repeat the inhale –*

*increase attention – hold attention – exhale – cycle two or three times, talking aloud.]*

**What did you see, what did you hear?**

*[Talk about any changes you see in the target spot, or the surrounding of the spot. Then model getting out of hypnosis. Blink your eyes and shake your arms. If necessary, repeat the model until the student is able to describe your physical activities doing the induction.]*

**Now it's your turn to enter hypnosis. You know what to do.**

**Look around the room, and pick a target spot to look at – one that appeals to you – that seems to stand out – that somehow just looks a little more obvious. It could be a light switch – a doorknob – anything that stands out clearly. You will know when you see it – you will notice a kind of settling and comfort – and when you get it, just smile and nod your head.**

***First cycle: Engage visual, auditory, and kinesthetic activity***

**Take a deep, long, slow breath. – Notice how, while you inhale – your chest lifts up – your shoulders come up – your back straightens, and you allow your head to rise toward the ceiling.**

*[Pace the student's breathing. Talk about lifting chest and shoulders, and raising heads, as the student inhales.]*

**Then, as you hold your eyes on your spot – exhale and hear the soft sounds of your breath – let your body relax down – deeper and softer – and float. Keep your eyes on your spot.**

*[Talk about relaxing, getting softer and floating down, as the student exhales.]*

*Second cycle: Strengthen visual, auditory, and kinesthetic activity, and begin inhibiting distractions*

**Increase visual focus on the spot, and inhale again. As you do – press down against the floor – and notice the little changes in your ankles – calves – as you rise upward from the seat. Allow the eyes to focus still more alertly on the spot – then – as you exhale – relax – float downward and listen to the softening sound of your breath. If, or whenever, your attention drifts away from the spot, say "NO" – Come back and hold attention to the spot. Take a long deep, slow breath – and let it out.**

*[Continue pacing the student's inhale and exhale.]*

*Third cycle: Increase visual, auditory, and kinesthetic activity and inhibition further*

**Increase attention even more on the spot – move your whole body up – by pushing down against the floor – and lifting the head up toward the ceiling. Even more alertly observe that spot – while you keep your conscious attention on the spot – exhale slowly and drift *down.* Your attention gets clearer and more focused. Remain in that consciously alert but relaxed condition – while your body breaths naturally and calmly. If your conscious mind drifts off the spot, say "NO" and go back to your spot – just float – relaxed – focusing your attention on the spot. You may or you may not notice that it gets easier and easier to keep your mind focused – the spot gets clearer – and the background fades.**

*[Continue pacing.]*

**Now blink your eyes, shake your arms, come out of hypnosis, and enjoy the change. Let's discuss your experience.**

*[Ask the student to process the three breathing cycles. Focus on what they noticed about changes in the target spot. With increasing attention, there should be a perceptible change in the physical appearance of the spot. It may get larger, and it may get clearer, there may be a small halo. That change is the sign that the student is getting into hypnosis. If the student does not recognize any change in the target, repeat the breathing cycle, with modifications, until the student is able to see and report change in the target.]*

***Skill 4: deepen your experience***

**Consider that you can increase the effect of hypnosis by becoming even more focused. Some people use the word "strengthening," or "intensifying" or "deepening." Things in the room around you become less noticeable. Your attention shifts to go intensely or deeply into your point of focus. In brief, to increase the experience and effects of alert hypnosis, you want to go deeper and deeper into focus. As you do, outside distractions have less effect. You have a growing sense of calmness.**

**What can you do to deepen your hypnosis? In general, simply adjust your attention into your spot, and notice what happens. Imagine a barrier around your spot – like the skin of an onion – or the layers of a pearl. Each time you exhale, imagine you are blowing off the top layer – with each breath – you get deeper – and deeper – and deeper into your spot.**

**With each breath, whisper or silently say the word "DEEPER." Time the word carefully, so that you get to the**

**end of the word at the same moment you get to the end of the exhalation. Listen to your voice, and notice the way you sound.**

**Use whatever metaphor for "deepening" is familiar and appropriate to you.**

**Some people want to know "How deep"?**

**They think of a scale from 0 to 10. Each number represents slightly deeper and narrower focus. Zero is focused as usual. Two is rather lightly focused on something. Five is strongly and deeply focused on something... some things seem to stand out, appear clearer. At 10 you are so deep that everything outside your point of focus almost disappears.**

*[At this point, you are introducing the analog scale of depth:*
*0 = focused as you usually are;*
*1 = slightly more focused then usual;*
*2 = rather lightly focused on something;*
*5 = strongly and deeply focused on something;*
*8 = very focused on something;*
*9 = very, very focused on something; and*
*10 = almost nothing outside your point of focus.]*

**Measuring your depth with the scale when you are doing hypnosis is simple. Just ask yourself "How deep in hypnosis am I?" Take the first number that pops into your mind. Some people say they can actually see a number, like time on a digital clock. Some report they can hear it, an internal voice calling out a number. Some report a feeling; a sort of knowing it is right. Report whatever feels right for you.**

*[Guide the student to simply accept, not overthink, the personal depth indicator. This is simply an ordinal scale, measuring greater than, or less than. The actual interval between the numbers is irrelevant. It is a measure that depth is getting deeper or shallower, no more exact than that.]*

**Now use the inhale – increase attention – hold attention – exhale cycle again. Check your depth before you start. Then whisper the word "deeper" with each exhalation – spacing your voice slowly – so that you finish the word – at the same time – you finish breathing out. Notice the depth scale number after three or four cycles.**

**Now blink your eyes and come on out of trance.**

*[Process the experience with the student. Repeat the exercise until he or she can get two or three levels deeper in hypnosis.]*

*Skill 5: Activate your goal*

**Now, while your body is relaxed and eyes are on the spot – relaxed – deeply focused – dip into memory – bring back that intention from the beginning of your work. Give breath – and voice – and body – and life – to your intention – stored in memory – just a few minutes ago.**

**Imagine yourself in that place, and time, and feeling – see the place – with all its color – and its fragrances. Maybe you can feel emotional involvement – you know what you are doing – and know you are doing it excellently. You can experience the sensations – and feel the pleasure – and anyone there – would see by your posture and expression – and hear in your voice – your satisfaction – and pleasure – the power of your intention to meet your goal. When you are immersed in that experience, comfortable, satisfied, doing well, enjoy it.**

*[Modify the instructions to make them congruent with the goal suggestion. Pace your instructions with the student's breathing.]*

**Now move your imagination forward in time – perhaps to a little later today – or tonight – or to sometime tomorrow – or even further in the future. Tell yourself how you will use your intention – what you will see and feel yourself doing – what pleasure you notice – how you carry out your intention. Experience the calm, tolerant, peaceful, excellent way you move and feel and think.**

*Skill 6: Live your change*

**Wouldn't it be nice if every time you did the cycle – what you were actively focusing on gets clearer – distracting thoughts fade – your intention gets more and more likely – more and more possible – more and more real. Maybe you can even carry out your intention while still in alert hypnosis.**

*[Depending on the situation, ask the student to stand up, move around the room, and engage in appropriate behavior. If this is the suggestion that involves reading, taking notes, writing, or doing some academic work, give the student a chance to read and explain the content while in alert hypnosis.]*

***Skill 7: Reorient back to the room and plan for next time***

**Now blink your eyes and come all the way back, paying attention to everything in the room. Review your experience with alert self-hypnosis.**

*[Exit hypnosis, and discuss the experience. Support and encourage any changes that the student reports. Help the student decide what worked, what did not work, and what changes to make the next time they practice.]*

## References

Alarcon, A., Capafons, A., Bayot, A., & Cardeña, E. (1999). Preference between two methods of active-alert hypnosis: Not all techniques are created equal. *American Journal of Clinical Hypnosis, 41,* 269-276.

Bányai, É., & Hilgard, E. R. (1976). A comparison of active-alert hypnotic induction with traditional relaxation induction. *Journal of Abnormal Psychology, 85,* 218-224.

Capafons, A. (1998). Auto-hipnosis rápida: un método de sugestión para el auto-control [Rapid self-hypnosis: A suggestion method for self-control]. *Psicothema, 10,* 571-581.

Cardeña, E., Alarcon, A., Capafons, A., & Bayot, A. (1998). Effects on suggestibility of a new method of active-alert hypnosis: Alert hand. *International Journal of Clinical & Experimental Hypnosis, 46,* 280-294.

Tart, C. (1970). Self-report scale of hypnotic depth. *International Journal of Clinical and Experimental Hypnosis, 18,* 105-125.

Unestahl, L.-E. (1983). *The mental aspects of gymnastics.* Orebro, Sweden: VEJE Publications.

Wark, D. (1989). Alert self-hypnosis techniques to improve reading comprehension. *Hypnos, 16,* 113-121.

Wark, D. M. (1990). Advanced comprehension suggestions for an alert trance. In D. C. Hammond (Eds.), *Handbook of hypnotic suggestions and metaphors* (p. 450). New York, NY: W.W. Norton.

Wark, D. M. (1998). Alert hypnosis: History and applications. In W. J. Matthews, & J. H. Edgette (Ed.), *Current thinking and research in brief therapy: Solutions, strategies, narratives* (pp. 287-304). Philadelphia, PA: Brunner/Mazel.

Wark, D. M., & Kohen, D. P. (2002). A spiral curriculum for hypnosis training. *American Journal of Clinical Hypnosis, 45,* 119-128.

## For Further Reading...

**Clinically, alert inductions have been used to treat:**

***1. Attention Deficit Hyperactivity Disorder***

Barabasz, A., & Barabasz, M. (1996). Neurotherapy and alert hypnosis in the treatment of attention deficit hyperactivity disorder. In S. J. Lynn, I. Kirsch, & J. Rhue (Eds.), *Casebook of clinical hypnosis* (pp. 217-292). Washington, DC: American Psychological Association.

***2. Combat post-traumatic stress disorder (PTSD)***

Eads, B. & Wark. D. M. (2015). Alert hypnotic inductions: Use in treating combat post-traumatic stress disorder. *American Journal of Clinical Hypnosis, 58,* 159-170.

***3. Education and test taking problems***

De Vos, H. M., & Louw, D. A. (2006). The effect of hypnotic training programs on the academic performance of students. *American Journal of Clinical Hypnosis, 49,* 101-112.

Wark, D. M. (1996). Teaching college students better learning skills using self-hypnosis. *American Journal of Clinical Hypnosis, 38,* 277-287.

Wark, D. M. (2011). Traditional and alert hypnosis for education: A literature review. *American Journal of Clinical Hypnosis, 54,* 96-106.

### *4. Habit control for smoking cessation and compulsive gambling*

Capafons, A., & Amigó, S. (1995). Emotional self-regulation therapy for smoking reduction: Description and initial empirical data. *International Journal of Clinical and Experimental Hypnosis, 43*, 7-19.

Lloret, D. E., Montesinos, R., & Capafons, A. (2014). Waking self-hypnosis efficacy in cognitive-behavioral treatment for pathological gambling: An effectiveness clinical assay. *International Journal of Clinical and Experimental Hypnosis, 62*, 50-69.

### *5. Public-speaking phobia*

Iglesias, A., & Iglesias, A. (2005). Awake-alert hypnosis in the treatment of panic disorder: A case report. *American Journal of Clinical Hypnosis, 47*, 249-257.

### *6. Psychotherapy*

Bányai, É., Zseni, A., & Túry, F. (1993). Active-alert hypnosis in psychotherapy. In J. W. Rhue, S. J. Lynn & I. Kirsch (Eds.), *Handbook of Clinical Hypnosis* (pp. 271-290). Washington, DC: American Psychological Association.

**Acknowledgments**

The author gratefully acknowledges the contributions of Jennifer Swaim, PhD, and Bruce Eads, MSW, to the preparation of this chapter.

# CHAPTER 7

# Suggestive Techniques Without Inductions for Medical Interventions

**Katalin Varga**

*Katalin Varga is a Professor at Eötvös Loránd University (ELTE), the head of the Department of Affective Psychology, and past President of the Hungarian Association of Hypnosis. She was awarded a Postgraduate Fellowship of the Hungarian Academy of Sciences (1986–1990) to study the subjective experiences associated with hypnosis and the role of suggestions in critical states. She was awarded her degree of "Doctor of University" (ELTE) in 1991, and a PhD in 1997 on comparing the subjective and behavioral effects of hypnosis.*

*As a member of the "Budapest hypnosis research laboratory," she is investigating hypnosis in an interactional framework, and in this multilevel approach she is focusing on the phenomenological data. For the past 20 years, she has been working with patients in a hospital setting—mostly critically ill patients—applying suggestive and hypnosis techniques. She is the founder and Professor of the postgraduate training of suggestive communication in somatic medicine, co-organized by the Hungarian Association of Hypnosis and Semmelweis University School of Medicine, Budapest. She has published numerous articles that present her research findings on hypnosis and clinical experiences on the application of suggestive techniques with the critically ill.*

* * *

*There is seldom, if ever, a need for a formalized or ritualistic technique.*

–Milton Erickson

*These patients are to be considered as people in hypnosis.*

–David Cheek

*In this state any statement may function as a powerful hypnotic suggestion.*

–Christel Bejenke

This chapter discusses to the use of suggestions *without* any formal hypnotic inductions. The idea is based on the observations made by many clinicians that, in many if not most medical situations, the patients (and their relatives) are already in a "trance" (altered state of consciousness); they are already exquisitely open to respond to suggestions, including both the helpful and less than helpful suggestions made by their health care providers.

Suggestions can be defined as the verbal or nonverbal messages given to a receiver which that receiver then involuntarily accepts and follows. It is important to clarify the primary types of suggestions in the health care context. These include: (1) suggestions provided in the context of formal hypnosis; (2) suggestions provided in the context of a therapeutic relationship (also known as therapeutic suggestions); and (3) general suggestions provided to patients that might not be intended as suggestions by the clinician providing those suggestions (Kekecs, Nagy, & Varga, 2014).

### Formal Hypnotic Suggestions

Formal hypnosis can be defined as any therapeutic interactions that include a component involving a ritual or "hypnotic induction" before the application of the key or specific suggestion(s), which is provided to increase the patient's response to the suggestions. In this case, the applied technique is overtly identified as "hypnosis"; usually, the words "hypnosis," "hypnotizing," and "hypnotic state" are explicitly stated, helping to define the context as clearly hypnotic (Farthing, 1992).

### Therapeutic Suggestions

Therapeutic suggestions can be defined as planned suggestions that are provided to the patient outside of the context of hypnosis; that is, not preceded by a hypnotic induction and not necessarily provided in a therapeutic context that is labeled as "hypnosis." However, such suggestions are meant to have a therapeutic (beneficial) impact and are given by a health care provider who is usually trained in techniques of suggestive communication. Typically, these are verbal statements that suggest beneficial changes or outcomes. However, they can also include suggestions embedded in an environment, including objects and nonverbal messages (e.g., eye contact, sighs, and touches) that can also have suggestive effects.

There are two subcategories of therapeutic suggestions:

1. Suggestions provided during a communication with the patient that provide important information (e.g., why radiation therapy is needed) that is provided in a way that follows the principles of effective suggestive communication; and
2. Suggestions that include something "extra" that are told to the patient over and above basic information about a medical intervention, and which are provided to enhance a beneficial effect or outcome. One example is a suggestion that the patient has an inner resource that can enhance recovery. Such "extra" suggestions can take many forms, such as that of a metaphor, helpful advice, or a story about another patient who recovered well, among others.

## General Suggestions

In addition to therapeutic suggestions made both within and outside of the hypnotic context, virtually all of the other patient communications—for example, the introduction of a clinic on a website, the decorations in the waiting room, the clothing worn by the health care providers, and the smell of and noises in the operating room, just to mention a few—may have a suggestive effect, even when these effects are unintended as well as hidden.

This chapter focuses on the latter two types of suggestions—that is, suggestions that are provided outside of the context of formal hypnosis—and how clinicians can take full advantage of their power to benefit their patients.

## How to Work with Spontaneous Trance States

Spontaneous trance in medical contexts is characterized by a focused state of consciousness and a temporary detachment from reality. An important feature of this trance state is the increase in one's sensitivity to suggestions. The feature makes suggestive communication a very effective tool for helping patients.

The clinical diagnosis of trance state can be based on contextual factors or behavioral signs. There are a number of contextual factors in most medical settings that can lead to an altered state of consciousness (see Bejenke, 1996a, 1996b; Cheek, 1969). They include:

- The planned use of highly complex and (to the patient) incomprehensible procedures;
- The presence of a significant disability due to the disease or presenting condition;
- The presence of a significant disability associated with the care itself (e.g., the patient is not able or allowed to leave the bed);
- An inability of the patient to speak;
- The presence of strong emotions, such as loneliness, fear, or anxiety; and
- A perceived loss of control.

The behavioral signs of a trance state include: symmetrical facial flaccidity, altered facial vascularity (usually pallor), generalized immobility, responsiveness to prescribed behaviors, relative absence of non-prescribed behaviors, and a long period of time (up to 15 to 30 sec) between a suggestion and a response (Bierman, 1989, p. 239). When such behavioral signs are observed or the setting is highly likely to result in the patient being in a trance and open to suggestions, it would seem to many clinicians that the next step is to offer a therapeutic suggestion at this point.

However, in this situation, two crucial things remain for the clinician to do. First, it is important to recognize that many times—perhaps even more often than not—the patient's attention is concentrated on pain, fear, and anxiety, and they do not necessarily know where they are or what is happening to them. In this situation, they may manifest a *negative* trance. Left alone, such a trance can contribute to negative outcomes. Thus, it is important for the clinician to facilitate a change in the tone of the state, to help the patient achieve a positive trance. This can be facilitated when the clinician helps the patient focus on peaceful or comfortable sensations and draws their attention to something pleasant, such as a good memory or a future valued goal.

The second thing that is essential is to build and maintain rapport; that is, a relationship of trust and connection between the patient and the health care professional. You know when this is happening when the patient and care provider are paying attention to each other, cooperating more and more, and synchronizing their interactions for a common goal, usually that of patient comfort and recovery.

There are a number of useful strategies for establishing, building, and maintaining rapport. The place to start, of course, is when the clinician first meets the patient. At this first contact, the clinician should introduce him- or herself and give a very short explanation of the reason for contacting the patient (e.g., "I am a psychologist; I came to make your stay in the hospital more comfortable.") Rapport building with patients in negative trance usually then continues with strategies that divert their attention. By catching their attention, we can then direct that attention to what we are saying and doing. By inviting patients to cooperate with us, we also motivate them, which strengthens the rapport. We can (and should) offer suggestions that they can accept; and being in a trance, the possibility that they will accept the suggestions is greatly increased. Such suggestions can include feeling more comfort, bleeding less or even stopping of bleeding, and relaxing the muscles, among many others. This way we can work with the patient and together set specific therapeutic goals.

The rapport that has been built should be maintained; it should nurture continuously, conveying to the patient that we are still working towards the same goal and that we appreciate the patient's cooperation. When our professional role ends, we should transfer rapport to the person who continues taking care of the patient, usually another health care professional or relative.

**Working Principles**

I have found the following working principles, as outlined by Cheek (1969), particularly useful.

- Avoid conversation or actions that might suggest you are pessimistic about the outcome;
- Collect your thoughts and marshal a plan of action *before* (!) touching or speaking directly to the patient;
- Tell the patient what has happened and that he or she will be all right;
- Outline what you are doing and your reason(s) for doing it;
- Provide medications for pain when possible;
- Encourage the patient to talk about the things they most enjoy, such as work, hobbies, or family.

It is also often useful to think of the "alternative" mode of consciousness and use the elements of such modes of consciousness (metaphors, models, visual, holistic images, etc.) for the benefit of the patient, especially when the "dominant" mode (critical analysis, logical explanations, verbal instructions) does not seem to be helpful (Unestahl, 1981).

In my practice, I often use the following principles to build positive suggestions for the patients I work with:

- Framing the medical environment into a "safe place" where the patient is "being cared for";
- Facilitate a sense of perceived control; prevent the development of learned helplessness;
- Explain all of the interventions and the reasons (i.e., to facilitate health and better outcomes) they are being offered;
- Reinforce communication at all levels; provide a response and feedback to all questions;
- Involve the patients in as many decisions as possible and as appropriate;
- Interpret and note treatment success, facilitating further motivation and expectations for recovery.

### Clinical Examples

In a classic study, a 30-second intervention proved to be very effective in an emergency situation (Jacobs, 1991). In this study, trained ambulance attendants were instructed to state the following to the injured person (independent of the injured person's conscious state):

> The worst is over. We are taking you to the hospital. Everything is being made ready. Let your body concentrate on repairing itself and feeling secure. ... Things are being made ready at the hospital for you. We're getting there as quickly and safely as possible. You are now in

> a safe position. The worst is over. (Jacobs, 1991, p. 8).

Comparisons between the usual care and the suggestion group showed an increased survival rate during transport to the hospital, a shorter hospital stay, and a faster recovery in favor of the suggestion group.

We can note that this intervention begins with a pacing-leading technique (connecting first to what likely may be of greatest concern to the patient) and then rapidly shifting the focus onto positive outcomes. The communication effectively applies the interspersal technique (that is, embedding suggestions with truisms, which is thought to increase the chances that the suggestions will be accepted) by mixing facts (e.g., we are taking you to the hospital) and positive suggestions (e.g., body repairing itself). The key message of "safety" is also repeated multiple times.

Gall (1990), a pediatrician, applies the following technique to ensure the cooperation of the child. Instead of waiting in his office for the "neeext patient," he goes out to the waiting room to the next child and asks the following set of questions:

- Is that you, Jennifer?
- Are you here today?
- Did you come here with your mother today?
- Are you walking with your mother now?
- Are you walking into my room?

Arriving in the doctor's office, he further builds on and utilizes the "enchantment" of the yes set:

- Are you getting up on my table?
- Are you sitting on the table?
- Are you looking up at the light?

And so on (Gall, 1990, p. 75).

Obviously, the primary goal here is to evoke and maintain a "yes set." The essence of the method is to elicit *agreement*. Referring to obvious facts (the patient's name, that she is here today, that she is with her mother, etc.) is one way to elicit the serial agreement of the patient, including agreement to the not so obvious parts (walking to the room, getting up to the table, looking up at the light).

Tannenbaum (1985) reports applying these techniques in private contexts as well, for example, with a woman who has been injured under her eye while playing volleyball. Tannenbaum describes approaching the person shortly after the injury, introducing himself as a doctor, and applying the suggestions without any induction:

> *You know, you have been injured near your eye* [states a trivial fact, it's the first part of a yes set], *and any injury near the eye should be examined by a physician* [the second part of the yes set]. *Now someone is gone to get some ice* [the third part of the yes set, it also justifies the need for special attention, and explains what kind of actions are undertaken to ensure her wellbeing] *and that can help to stop the swelling* [the main suggestion prepared by the yes set, it marks the main goal]. *And later you can go to the emergency room to be examined* [sets the

> timeframe and indicates what she should do next] *so you can be sure that everything is all right* [getting better is not just a possibility, it's a fact]. *But right now there's really nothing you need to do* [she is unable to do anything at the moment, but Tanenbaum reframes it so that his words imply that nothing needs to be done, everything will be all right without her intervening] *so you could just imagine yourself lying comfortably in a pleasant place at the beach or in the mountains* [he guides her attention with the imaginative technique and to help her control the pain]. (Added text in brackets, Tanenbaum, 1985. p. 442; comments, Varga, 2011, p. 15).

In another similar case, Tannenbaum helps a ballet dancer who has twisted his ankle (Tannenbaum, 1985). Again, without any induction the rapport formation is based on the main motivation of the dancer (to feel better):

> *I asked if I could do 'something to help your ankle feel better,'* [he starts with a simple question, but with the positivity it implies that if he helps the dancer will get better]... *Now* [he gently elevates the injured leg] *there is nothing you need to do but let your ankle remain elevated so it can begin to feel better and heal quickly* [the dancer will feel better almost effortlessly]. *After you get home* [the next step is placed in the near future] *you can put some ice on it so it can continue to heal* [implicating that the healing process has already been started]. *Now you don't know how it will heal* [his leg will heal perfectly without

> any conscious effort], *but you can just take some relaxing breaths* [this suggests that breathing is relaxing; a therapeutic bind, because it is not possible to avoid breathing, so the patient cannot help becoming increasingly relaxed] *and feel confident that your subconscious mind can do whatever is necessary* [again, the positive processes are working without conscious intervention] *to allow your ankle to feel better and function adequately.* [It is also noteworthy that the word "heal" is repeated frequently in succession to strengthen the main suggestion.] (Added text in brackets, Tanenbaum, 1985, p. 444; comments, Varga, 2011, p. 15).

## Some Additional Examples from my Practice

In this section, I present some additional examples from my practice, which are described in more detail in a recent book (Varga, 2015). Note that the names of the patients have been changed to protect their identity.

### Luis

Luis was an 18-year-old patient. He had lost consciousness reportedly as a result of heroin overdose, and he had been flat on his side for so long that his left arm had gangrened and had to be amputated from the shoulder down. He spent 2 weeks in a coma in the hospital ICU. After the amputation, I was asked to see him because he was extremely depressed and expressed suicidal urges. Clearly, waking up from coma and finding the absence of one's arm would result in a very negative state.

When I entered his room in the intensive care unit, he was sitting in a wheelchair with a very sad body posture, with his head bent down. As I approached him and sat down next to him, he barely looked up at me. I introduced myself:

"I am Katalin Varga, a psychologist. Your doctor asked me to contact you." I then asked: "How do you think we could cooperate more efficiently: if we are on a first-name basis or otherwise, on a more formal basis?" The establishment of rapport was facilitated by the introduction (introducing myself and giving my profession and reason for seeing that patient; all facts). It was followed by a therapeutic double-bind question (asking the patient to express a preference regarding us being less or more formal with each other). It did not matter which of the offered alternatives the patient chose; what matters is the success of the cooperation that the question engenders. Moreover, underlying the question was an implication of a longer cooperation, which, in the current situation, projects an essential positive perspective about the future for the patient.

He chose the first-name basis option. I continued by asking: "What do your friends call you?" (He told me: Luis). "Can I call you that, too?" I asked. He nodded, which meant to me that he "said yes" to the covert, implied message that the cooperation would be amicable. Regarding the initial negative state, and that it was not him who had originally requested psychological support, it was extremely important to establish a frame of our cooperation. My introductory questions aimed to create a collaborative relationship, a good rapport. Following this, an honest and pleasant conversation started, and we agreed to work together to help him cope with this new life (!) situation. This latter part included formal hypnosis sessions, mostly for soothing the pain in his leg on the same side of his amputated arm. Our cooperation lasted through the rehabilitation period and involved six sessions.

**Tom**

Tom was a 24-year-old patient who was being treated in the ICU. Following a brain varicose vein thrombosis, he was out of his initial coma and on his way to recovery. We met several times, including during his comatose period. I supported him with positive suggestions, describing the ICU as a safe place and explaining the aim of treatment in positive terms, reframing coma as a resting state that he needed to rearrange his homeostasis.

On one occasion when I entered the hospital, his doctor told me that he had been very unwell during the recent couple of hours. He looked very frightened. His body was trembling, he was sweating, his right arm was tensed into a fist, and his pulse was 220 beats per minute (bpm). In his left hand, there was a spiky plastic ball that he kept rubbing against his chest. His skin was red with irritation caused by this ball.

It was clear that Tom was in a negative trance state. Fortunately, we had already established good rapport from prior interactions. I stood on his right side and his best friend stood on his left. As I started to speak, following some comments that the friend was making, I said to the patient repeatedly in a calm voice, "Paul (his friend) is standing on your left side, and I'm on your *right*. You can hear my voice from the *right*, and his from the left." Thus, I begin with a very simple description of his current (physical) orientation, while associating myself with the patient's friend. As all this is factual information, the initial sentence also serves as an initiation of a yes set.

I continued with the following, while softly stroking the patient's tense right arm.

> Now your hand is shaking... you must feel a little vibration in it... this is a sign that you've begun to move your *right* side... This is going to be all *right* here too... from day to day you will be able to move your *right* hand more and more.

Our rapport was strengthened by the physical contact. Also, by relying on the double meaning of the word "right," I sought to further lead the patient's attention. By replacing the tension and pain of the arm with positive associations (right), I intended to lessen the unpleasant symptoms. I reframed the cramp as the sign of recovery, providing a positive future orientation.

After 5 to 10 minutes, the patient started to relax. The effectiveness of suggestions was observed in his physical signs and on the monitor: he calmed down, his facial features smoothed out, he closed his eyes, and his pulse decreased to 83 bpm. In this pleasant and positive altered state, we continued with general suggestions to support recovery.

**Alex**

The ICU asked for psychological consultation in the treatment of a 24-year-old man suffering from Guillain-Barré syndrome (an autoimmune disorder with paralysis, including respiratory muscles, with the patient's full awareness). According to his doctors, the patient suffered from depression and could not cope with immobility, assisted breathing, speechlessness, and helplessness. I saw him every other day for 4 months, and we also prepared audio recordings for him to listen to between sessions. One day when I entered the unit, the patient's wife met me and was very agitated. She told me that the patient was planning on leaving the hospital, abandoning his treatment.

When I arrived at his bed, the exhausted man immediately whispered to me, "They want to kill me. Take me away from here! They suck my blood and sell it abroad."

With floundering in this way, he was clearly in a trance state, and an extremely negative one. This state is common among patients who have spent weeks lying in a bed, motionless and only able to see the ceiling. His concern—that his doctors were killing him and were selling his blood—was based on a misunderstanding; perhaps some mixture of mishearing or misinterpreting something that was said within his earshot but that was not meant for his ears, a fantasy or dream that he had, or some combination of these elements.

We had already developed good rapport, which I made use of in this tense situation. Instead of trying to convince him that he was mistaken, I accepted what he said and asked him, "Why do you think so?" This was intended to be a first step towards finding a solution to the problem. On the surface, it might appear the opposite of what we are ultimately trying to achieve, but, in fact, this gives him the feeling that he is being listened to and taken seriously (an example of the "pacing" phase of the pacing-leading technique).

He told me, "Too much blood is drawn from me, and I heard that they are planning to sell it abroad."

I told him, "I think this is very unlikely to be true because I know the hospital staff very well. In addition to this, your blood is not of good enough quality to be sold, which is the very reason it is being cleaned." Being a psychologist not formally attached to the Unit, I can be an effective "mediator;" it allows me to work for the patient while caring for the interest of the hospital.

My comments intended to strengthen his reality orientation by very strongly implying that his assumption—that was just elicited in the pacing part—was incorrect. At the same time, it also served as a reminder that he is here as a patient needing treatment. This became the leading phase of the intervention, which was my real aim: to help him understand that he needed to stay in the hospital and undergo treatment.

I offered, "Let me ask your doctors about the details of these blood samples, and based on these we can make a good decision." So what had been "his problem" became "our problem." With his agreement to my proposal, we agreed that we would make any decision about his treatment *together* (cooperation).

I asked his doctor many questions about the blood samples, including why and when his blood was drawn. His doctor responded to my questions and also showed me all the tubes and medical charts. I was in fact quite surprised by the large number of tests that were being conducted in addition to the usual routine tests. I took all these tubes—as object suggestions—back to the patient, and explained the situation to him in detail, including everything I learned from his physicians. By providing this information, I was able to support the patient's (positive) reality orientation. During the explanation, he became more and more calm. I ended by building a yes set that lead to the desired aim; the patient ended up agreeing to stay in the hospital and continue undergoing the treatment needed for his health and welfare.

KV: So, do you understand why now?

Patient: Yes.

KV: Do you see why your blood needs to be constantly drawn?

Patient: Yes.

KV: Is the situation any easier to bear now?

Patient: Yes.

KV: Will you stay?

Patient: Yes.

KV: So the treatment can continue, can't it?

Patient: Yes it can.

I also wanted to involve the patient's wife, as she was also very concerned about her husband's distress and agitation. So, I invited his wife (and also his mother) into the room and asked the patient the same questions as above. By repeating the conversation, we could reassure the relatives that the situation was now clear and that Alex wanted to participant in continued treatment.

I ended this session by telling the patient, "Please feel free to ask any questions of who you feel you can trust the most, should it be the nurse, doctor, or me, and we will find answers for you." The format of the "question or query" weakens the edge of the current, desperately mistrustful situation (reframing). Moreover, closing in this way offers a wide range of specialists who could provide reassuring answers to future questions, no matter whom he might choose (a therapeutic double-bind). This also serves as another way to orient him to the future, which indirectly suggests survival as well as continued acceptance of staying in the hospital for treatment.

## Summary and Conclusions

Although the examples presented here are with critically ill patients, it is important to stress that practically any area of medicine can (and should!) use positive suggestions in daily communication. As should be obvious, positivity is not sugarcoating otherwise sad facts about the patient's condition or situation. Instead, it is about explaining the situation in a future-oriented way and leading towards a positive outcome or established goal. Importantly, a negative trance state, when present, can be utilized, because when present a negative trance state is associated with the patient being open to suggestions. After rapport building, the therapeutic suggestions can be offered immediately for the patient's benefit. Although the use of this technique might be questioned from an ethical perspective, because we are applying (hypnotic) suggestions without getting informed consent from the patient, it is important to understand that patients respond to our suggestions at all times and in all of our day-to-day interactions with them—including unfortunately the negative messages. The examples presented in this chapter clearly show that the suggestions were all meant to achieve something beneficial for the patient (e.g., providing emotional support for accepting an otherwise terrible situation [Luis], managing pain and physiological discomfort [Tom], (re)establishing reality orientation supporting the acceptance of treatment [Alex]). It is important that clinicians be aware of the powerful effects of their words and apply this awareness for the benefit of their patients.

## References

Bejenke, C. J. (1996a). Painful medical procedures. In J. Barber (Ed.), *Hypnosis and suggestion in the treatment of pain* (pp. 209–265). New York, NY: W. W. Norton and Company.

Bejenke, C. J. (1996b). Preparation of patients for stressful medical interventions: Some very simple approaches. In B. Peter, B. Trenkle, F. C. Kinzel, C. Duffner, & A. Iost-Peter (Eds.), *Hypnosis international monographs No 2: Munich lectures on hypnosis and psychotherapy* (pp. 27–36). Munich, Germany: MEG-Stiftung.

Bierman, S. F. (1989). Hypnosis in the emergency department. *American Journal of Emergency Medicine, 7,* 238–242.

Cheek, D. B. (1969). Communication with the critically ill. *American Journal of Clinical Hypnosis, 12,* 75–85.

Farthing, G. W. (1992). Altered states of consciousness. In G. W. Farthing (Ed.), *The psychology of consciousness* (pp. 202–219). Englewood Cliffs, NJ: Prentice-Hall.

Gall, J. C. (1990). The art of examining a child: Use of naturalistic methods in the pediatric physical examination. *Ericksonian Monographs, 7,* 69–85.

Jacobs, D. T. (1991). *Patient communication for first responders and EMS personnel*. Englewood Cliffs, NJ: Prentice-Hall.

Kekecs, Z., Nagy, T., & Varga, K. (2014). The effectiveness of suggestive techniques in reducing post-operative side effects: A meta-analysis of randomized controlled trials. *Anesthesia & Analgesia, 119,* 1407–1419.

Tanenbaum, B. L. M. (1985). Ericksonian techniques in emergency situations: Pain control. In J. K. Zeig (Ed.), *Ericksonian psychotherapy, volume II: Clinical applications* (pp. 439–447). New York, NY: Bruner/Mazel.

Unestahl, L. E. (1981). *Inner mental training*. Örebro, Sweden: Veje Publishing.

Varga, K. (2011). *Beyond the words: Communication and suggestion in medical practice*. New York, NY: Nova Science Publishers.

Varga, K. (2015). *Communication strategies in medical settings*. Frankfurt am Main, Germany: Peter Lang.

**For Further Reading...**

Ewin, D. M. (1986). Emergency room hypnosis for the burned patient. *American Journal of Clinical Hypnosis, 29*, 7–11.

Ewin, D. M. (2011). The laws of hypnotic suggestion. In K. Varga (Ed.), *Beyond the words: Communication and suggestion in medical practice* (pp. 75–82). New York, NY: Nova Science Publisher.

Hammond, D. C. (1990). *Hypnotic suggestions and metaphors*. New York, NY: W. W. Norton and Company.

Józsa, E. (2011). The concept and role of rapport in medical communication. In K. Varga (Ed.), *Beyond the words: Communication and suggestion in medical practice* (pp. 57–74). New York, NY: Nova Science Publisher.

Kekecs, Z., & Varga, K. (2013). Positive suggestion techniques in somatic medicine: A review of the empirical studies. *Interventional Medicine and Applied Science, 5*, 101–111.

Ludwig, A. M. (1969). Altered states of consciousness. In C. Tart (Ed.), *Altered states of consciousness: A book of readings* (pp. 9–22). New York, NY: Wiley.

Poncelet, N. M. (1985). An Ericksonian approach to childbirth. In J. Zeig (Ed.), *Ericksonian psychotherapy II.: Clinical applications, 18*, 267–285.

Schlanger, J., Fritúz, G., & Varga, K. (2013). Therapeutic suggestion helps to cut back on drug intake for mechanically ventilated patients in intensive care unit. *Interventional Medicine and Applied Science, 5,* 145–152.

Szeverényi, Cs., Csernátony, Z., Balogh, Á., & Varga, K. (2013). Examples of positive suggestions given to patients undergoing orthopaedic surgeries. *Interventional Medicine and Applied Science, 5,* 112–115.

Szilágyi, A., Diószeghy, C., Fritúz, G., Gál, J., & Varga K. (2014). Shortening the length of stay and mechanical ventilation time by using positive suggestions via MP3 players for ventilated patients. *Interventional Medicine and Applied Science, 6,* 3–15.

Varga, K. (2004). The possible explanation of metaphors in re-interpreting negative life events: Our experiences with the critically ill. *Hypnos, 31,* 201–207.

Varga, K. (2013). Suggestive techniques connected to medical interventions. *Interventional Medicine and Applied Science, 5,* 95–100.

Varga, K., Varga, Zs., & Fritúz, G. (2013). Psychological support based on positive suggestions in the treatment of a critically ill ICU patient: A case report. *Interventional Medicine and Applied Science, 5,* 153–161.

# CHAPTER 8

# The "3 and 6" Hypnotic Induction Technique for Children and Adolescents

**Daniel P. Kohen**

*"Dr. Dan" Kohen is retired Professor of Pediatrics and Family Medicine and Community Health, and director of DBP Fellowship Training, University of Minnesota. Following 35 years in academia, he maintains a private practice in Minneapolis. Dr. Kohen is sought after as a key speaker/faculty, author, and clinician. He has held leadership roles in the American Society of Clinical Hypnosis (ASCH), the Minnesota Society of Clinical Hypnosis (MSCH) and the American Board of Medical Hypnosis.*

*For 30 years, he was the MSCH Director of Education and Training. He is a Fellow in the ASCH, the American Academy of Pediatrics, and the Society for Clinical and Experimental Hypnosis (SCEH). Dr. Kohen has taught all around the U.S. and Canada and in 12 countries around the world for over 38 years. With Dr. Pam Kaiser, he spearheaded the emergence and evolution of the premier training organization for pediatric clinical hypnosis, the National Pediatric Hypnosis Training Institute (NPHTI) (www.nphti.org), a 501c3 nonprofit organization.*

*Dr. Kohen coauthored (with Dr. Karen Olness) the definitive text on pediatric hypnosis,* Hypnosis & Hypnotherapy with

Children, 4th ed. *(2011), which also has been translated into and published in French and German. He has authored over 90 published articles, book chapters, and abstracts. Dr. Kohen and Dr. Kaiser recently published an important summary article on the use of clinical hypnosis with children, entitled "Clinical hypnosis with children and adolescents—What? Why? How?: Origins, applications, and efficacy" (Kohen and Kaiser, 2014).*

* * *

The essential ingredients of an effective hypnotic induction with children/adolescents are that it is:

1. Tailored to the developmental level/maturation of the child/teen;
2. Offered in the context of evolving rapport with the child, most notably focused upon developing an understanding and genuine, authentic interest in the child's favorite activities in which to become absorbed (e.g. hobbies, sports, music, crafts, etc.) and identification of the child's strengths;
3. Sensitive to, and aware of, the child's motivation and positive expectations for change; and
4. Evocative of curiosity.

### Tailored to the Developmental Level/Maturation of the Child/Teen

Talking about the essence/feeling of hypnosis as being analogous to the feeling of "pretending" is necessary and entirely appropriate for a preschooler, (e.g., a child aged 3-5 or 6 years), and parent of that preschooler. On the other hand, the same language with a typically developing pre-teen or teenager would likely be perceived as demeaning, insulting, and even absurd. With a middle-aged child of 7-12 years of age, talking about "daydreaming on purpose" is congruent with where this age group of children "live their lives." With adolescents, talking about imagination and in the current parlance of teenager (e.g., "zoning out," "spacing out," etc.) is likely to capture their attention and drive the credibility of the clinician in a positive direction. With both "middle age" children and adolescents, it is often very helpful for the clinician to explain and clarify their role as the clinician as, for example, an "Imagination Coach" (Bob Deutsch, personal communication).

**Offered in the Context of Evolving Rapport with the Child**

Without positive rapport, no clinician really has a right to expect any child (or teen, or adult) to listen to, or "go along with," *anything* they suggest, recommend, or teach, much less hypnosis. It is always the clinician's job to foster and facilitate the development of rapport from the very beginning of what will become the therapeutic relationship; and to nurture it, discovering with time when it is appropriate and when there is a readiness to proceed with introducing and teaching a [self] hypnotic induction technique.

To be sure, the ingredients and nature of rapport will vary with the cultures, personalities, and all of the individual idiosyncrasies, likes, and dislikes of both clinician and patient. The successful clinician will be the one who listens the most; he or she becomes genuinely engaged and absorbed in the child/youth's story about who they are, what they do, what they enjoy, and what they're best at doing. In so doing, the successful clinician leads and paces this conversation, is alert to—and mindful of—the nature and quality of the child's absorption, gently guiding it toward readiness to introduce hypnotic approaches or to evolve into a naturalistic hypnotic experience.

## Sensitive to the Child's Motivation and Positive Expectations for Change

As part of the evolution of their rapport the clinician and child (and parents) should carefully clarify the nature of the presenting problem(s) and concern(s), and especially the *child's personal perspective, desire to improve, and willingness to create change(s) toward solving the problem*. For example, in the context of an initial, getting-to-know-you/rapport-building first visit, I usually find a way to ask the following questions regarding their attitudes about their presenting concerns:

1. Do you think you have had this (pain, headaches, anxiety about school, bed-wetting, etc.) long enough?
2. Is there anything GOOD about it?
3. Do you NEED IT for anything?
4. Are you going to MISS IT WHEN it's GONE?

Far and away, the most common answers are YES, NO!, NO!!, and NO!!! respectively. With the gentle use of humor, I may clarify the reasons for asking by noting, "Great, I wanted to know because if you NEED them or they have some value and you'll miss them when they're gone, then I don't want to waste your time or mine helping to get rid of them if you NEED them. On the other hand, if you DO NOT NEED them, they have NO VALUE, and you WON'T MISS THEM, then I am 100% sure I can help you to help yourself."

## Evoke Curiosity

Although each of the four essential ingredients of effective inductions I list are noted sequentially, they are interwoven. Indeed, for this writer, the evolution of rapport begins as early as the first moments I meet the patient in the waiting room. Before one meets a new child/teen patient, one should know at least what the presenting concern is and the age of the child. This gives me some idea of what I *might* reasonably expect upon going to the waiting room to meet and greet the child and whoever has accompanied him or her. With this in mind, I commonly come to the waiting room, and look around while saying, "Hi, I'm looking for someone named ________. Are there any _________'s out here?" The person named will inevitably identify him- or herself and how this is done is predictably reflective of their age and, more important, their level of development, and, sometimes, of their attitude about being there.

My purposeful, conscious intention to evoke curiosity (about me, this office, and this about-to-happen visit) includes looking for the child this way, introducing myself to them, asking them who the people are with them and asking them to introduce me to their mother or father or whoever else may have accompanied them. My intention is that as they become more curious, they will be that much more engaged in, attentive to, and absorbed in our evolving communication. In the process, *my* expectation is that this will positively influence and "drive" the development of our rapport toward the kind of effective communication that will nurture the hypnotic approach and work to be unfolded.

**The "3 and 6" Induction with Commentary**

I teach the "3 and 6" pediatric hypnosis induction technique frequently to children and adolescents, particularly because, as I tell children (key words for emphasis are in *italics* or **CAPITAL LETTERS**).

**Clinician: This will be VERY easy to learn.**

*[Of course telling the child about the induction is really part of the induction and is very effective because it is naturalistic, part of our conversation, not mysterious or "weird." And, it is offered in the context of a new but emerging positive relationship in which a measure of positive rapport has already been established (as noted earlier, an essential feature for any induction). Moreover, it is presented with the continuing intention of evoking curiosity, another ingredient in developing the focused attention that is integral to an effective induction strategy.]*

**It does NOT require any special new things...** ***everything you need to know to do it, you already know*** **—you just don't know (yet) that you already know, but as soon as you do, then you'll know that you knew it before but just didn't know that you knew. And then, it won't be new, you know?**

*[Although this is at once playful (with word-play), matter-of-fact, and completely "true" and is presented that way, i.e. matter-of-factly, it is nonetheless at the same time also purposefully confusional and as such designed to capture and gain focused attention, essential to all hypnotic "inductions" (beginnings). If the child is confused and becomes less focused, the natural response is/should be reassurance such as "no worries, you'll see in a few moments how easy this is."]*

**All you need in order to learn and do this and then use it is** ***your breathing,*** **which, after all, you have with you ALL THE TIME. And, you need** ***your focus,*** **which you know you have and how to use. And,** ***you need to want to BECAUSE*** ***when*** **you learn it** ***then*** **you can** ***find out*** **how to** ***use it and*** **about** ***HOW it can help you*** **with... [whatever their problem is].**

**Are you ready to learn?**

*[This is a question both about "Are you listening and paying attention?" and about motivation and positive expectations; it is almost universally responded to in a positive manner.]*

**This is called the "3 and 6." So, first I am going to describe it in detail and tell you all that you will need to know about it—so please do NOT do it now, just LISTEN.**

*[Sometimes I purposely make a tangent and point out the FUN that the word LISTEN uses the same exact letters—when rearranged—that spell the word SILENT which is of course necessary in order to LISTEN well! Sometimes I will print S-I-L-E-N-T and then L-I-S-T-E-N and give it to them to take home.]*

**So, the "3" stands for taking a breath in through your nose, slowly and evenly, and counting slowly to 3. NOT a totally deep breath, NOT holding your breath, NOT 3 breaths... remember, don't do this yet.**

**Like this...**

*[Demonstrate breathing in and slowly counting to 3 with fingers.]*

**"And" stands for "and" that's it!**

*[Observe the child's face to make sure they "get" this.]*

**The "6" stands for breathing out through your mouth slowly through lips pursed like you're going to kiss—not 6 breaths or holding your breath for 6 seconds but just a slow *count to 6 as you breathe out... Okay, got it? The in-breath slow count to 3 and the out-breath, slow count to 6.***

***NOW I'll demonstrate...***

*[Demonstrate the entire breathing exercise.]*

**"3" is: First, breathe in through my nose, and slowly count to 3...**

**Count on your fingers to demonstrate.**

**"and" is and...**

**Then, "6" is breathe OUT through my lips like I'm going to kiss, for slow count to 6.**

*[Show counting to 6 on fingers.]*

**Now, that's the *first breath* of the "3 and 6." For the *second "3 and 6," breath* you do exactly the same thing but *with your eyes closed*. Having the eyes closed *kind of shuts things out that are around you and might otherwise distract you from FOCUS; and of course when your eyes are closed this allows you to see things more clearly inside your mind*.**

*[These explanatory comments also have obvious double-meanings/ intentions. From one perspective, one might call this an intensification or "deepening" strategy but they are also an integral part of the induction training.]*

**For the third "3 and 6," you do it the same way, keep your eyes closed, and *while* you are doing the "3 and 6" you let your mind imagine some place where you really like to be, who you're with, what you're doing there *because doing THIS helps the "3 and 6" to work even better*. When you are there in your mind's imagination, you can notice what you see, what you hear, what you feel, what you smell, and what you taste there.**

**For the fourth "3 and 6," you do it the same way, only this time while you're doing the "6" part, and breathing out slowly to the slow count to 6, you notice how your shoulders naturally go down as you breathe out...**

*[Can say "exhale" for an older child or teen.]*

**and you pay attention to the way the tension naturally goes away and the way your body relaxes as you breathe out.**

**Then, after the fourth "3 and 6," you just *stay there,* enjoying imagining wherever you are, noticing the natural way your shoulders relax and *then the relaxing feeling spreads more down* your body with each next breath.**

**And *while* you're doing that, *this is the time when inside your imagination you can give important messages or instructions to your body or mind about what things you want to change that are really important to you, because that is MUCH EASIER to do when you are in your imagination and self-hypnosis this way.***

**Okay, have you got it? I'll go through all the steps I just told you about as I demonstrate it—don't do it YET—and THEN it will be your turn and I'll help you.**

*[Of course these are all now hypnotic suggestions though they are "officially" learning the induction technique. "I'll help you" is the reassurance that the coach will be there to guide and the "anchor" to the hypnotic suggestion.]*

**So, first breathe in slowly through the nose to a slow count to 3.**

*[Demonstrate, count on fingers.]*

**Then, "and"...**

**Then, breathe out through your pursed lips to a slow count to 6.**

*[Demonstrate, count on fingers.]*

**The second "3 and 6" is the same with eyes closed.**

*[Demonstrate.]*

**The third "3 and 6" is the same with focus on favorite imagination.**

*[Demonstrate.]*

**The fourth "3 and 6" is to notice relaxation in shoulders during breathing out.**

*[Demonstrate, with obvious, even exaggerated drooping of shoulders during exhalation.]*

**Then stay there.**

*[Demonstration of two or three additional breaths.]*

**Any questions? Okay, it's your turn to DO IT, go ahead and start and I will help by talking to you along the way:**

***First "3 and** 6."*

*[Clinician compliments that done right, well and/or, e.g., suggests, "Good, and a little more slowly."]*

***Second "3 and** 6."*

*[As the eyes close, compliment and suggest something about visualization and seeing things clearly "inside" your mind.]*

***Third "3 and 6"*... see where you are, who you're with... what you're doing... hear the sounds there, maybe voices, maybe music, I don't know, but you'll know... Smell the smells whether it's spring or summer or winter or fall, maybe the smell of something cooking or your favorite snack, and taste the tastes as though you were eating right now, and feel the feelings—sitting, walking, and running.**

*[Clinician suggests multisensory imagery for experiencing a favorite activity. Of course, this should be tailored to each child's interests.]*

***Fourth "3 and 6"—Noticing relaxation.***

*[Progressive relaxation, intensification (deepening).]*

**That's right! Nicely done... NOW just keep enjoying being there, *letting* the relaxing *move down your body* just right for you, more and more with each next breath OUT... right... and you don't even have to do "3 and 6" on purpose because your mind and body have learned so well and it's great to know that you are doing it *exactly right* and that it gets *even easier to do every time you do it.***

*[Posthypnotic suggestion.]*

***I don't know if you'll practice this 3 to 4 times every day for 5 minutes or maybe 2 or 3, but you'll find out.***

*[Posthypnotic suggestion for practice self-hypnosis.]*

**The last thing you need to know before you finish for today...**

*[Suggestion to prepare for termination of the trance.]*

**is that every time you do the "3 and 6" it gets easier and easier...**

*[Posthypnotic suggestion.]*

**because everyone knows that's how you get better at anything, doing it over and over and more and more;**

*[Motivating suggestion.]*

**AND *because* you always have your breath with you. IF you are practicing "3 and 6" in the daytime for a few minutes, then after you do it you can just open your eyes and feel refreshed, like you just had a half-hour nap!**

**And IF you are practicing it at BEDTIME you don't even have to stop, you can just let it drift *on its own* into a wonderful peaceful night's sleep with a great dream.**

**And, then when you're finished, you'll be done.**

*[Clinician stops talking and waits for patient to alert, which they always do!]*

## References

Kohen, D. P., & Kaiser, P. (2014). Clinical hypnosis with children and adolescents—What? Why? How?: Origins, applications, and efficacy. *Children, 1,* 74-98.

## For Further Reading...

Culbert, T., & Olness, K. (Eds). (2009). *Integrative pediatrics* (Weil Integrative Medicine Library). New York, NY: Oxford University Press.

Kohen, D. P., & Olness, K. N. (2011). *Hypnosis and hypnotherapy with children* (4th ed). New York, NY: Routledge.

Sugarman, L. I. & Wester, W. C. (Eds). (2013). *Therapeutic hypnosis with children and adolescents* (2nd ed.). Carmarthen, Wales: Crown House,

Yapko, M. D. (2012). *Trancework: An introduction to the practice of clinical hypnosis* (4th ed.). New York, NY: Routledge.

# CHAPTER 9

# Hypnotic Inductions for Families: Integrating Systemic Disconnections in the Family Mind

**Camillo Loriedo**

*Camillo Loriedo has used hypnosis as a part of his family and general psychological practice for over 35 years. Although his primary interest was in family therapy when he began his training, one of his professors gave him a book on hypnosis (*Uncommon Therapy*, by Jay Haley) to be translated into Italian, and he found it fascinating. So he sought and obtained training in hypnosis when he was still in graduate school.*

*One day, a professor who knew that he had an interest and skills in both family therapy and hypnosis called him on the phone and asked him to try hypnosis with a schizophrenic child that the professor was seeing at that very moment. He agreed and said he would be available to see the child the next day, but his professor asked him to work with the child right then, on the phone. Dr. Loriedo was extremely hesitant, but his supervising professor insisted. So Dr. Loriedo performed an induction, listening carefully to the way that the child was breathing as feedback.*

*Once he thought that the child was hypnotized, he made some positive suggestions and then realerted and thanked the child. The next day, he asked his professor how the child and family responded. The professor told him that the effects were astonishing. Not only did the child seem to go into a deep trance and respond positively to the suggestions, but the whole family, who was intensely watching the child, also seemed to go into trance.*

*This had the added benefit of improving the whole tenor of the family interaction. After that, Dr. Loriedo began regularly using hypnosis as a part of his family therapy as well as his individual psychotherapy practice. He has developed over the years, as described below, a number of hypnotic inductions that can be used to provide an important impetus for positive change in the family.*

* * *

The classic description of induction as a preparation and introduction to the trance state and as considered distinct from the hypnotic experience—like anesthesia provided before a medical procedure—has never set that well with me. In my experience, the induction *is* therapy. I consider it as a fundamental part of hypnotic treatment. More than this, the induction facilitates a foundation of *rapport*; the way the clinician guides the client inside the hypnotic reality and the way the client responds to this guide gives the hypnotic relationship its particular shape.

### Interactional Phenomenon Produced by a Family Induction

A hypnotic induction with an entire family produces a number of specific phenomena that have interesting and useful effects on family dynamics (Loriedo, 2008). Individual hypnosis also tends to produce specific phenomena such as breathing-rhythm modifications, perceived relaxation, specific ocular patterns, among many others; but the interactive impact of hypnosis cannot be seen when we only observe the individual changes.

### Physical Synchronism

Regardless of the induction technique, when used with family systems, hypnosis tends to increase the frequency of the interactional phenomenon of the *isomorphic positions* described by Albert Scheflen (1973) and named *synchronic behaviors* by Adam Kendon (1979); that is, individual movements, gestures, and/or postural shifts that are reproduced by others in a chain of simultaneous activities. At the same time, we also observe a strong reduction of dysrhythmic behaviors (Birdwistell, 1970).

### Emotional Attunement

Synchronic behaviors provide visual evidence of an increasing harmony. But this effect brings with it a further synchronization at the affective level. For example, I have observed that family interviews after a conjoint hypnotic session reveal that participants frequently report very similar emotions and feelings.

### Conjoint Activity and Increased Sense of Togetherness

When family members are asked by the therapist to develop shared activities, they often report a new or increased sense of connection that is likely rooted in both behavioral synchronisms and emotional attunement. Families that have shared a *hypnotic* experience also demonstrate an even greater sense of connection, as well as an increased ability to work conjointly.

### Increased Attention to Content

In systemic family therapy, an ability to focus on the content of communication is a further advantage that the collective hypnotic induction can produce. The trance state induces in individual family members an increased ability to listen with more intense attention; it is easier for family members to understand the meanings conveyed by other communicants during the session. Family therapists know that dysfunctional families take the opposite direction; for dysfunctional families, a given communication can be accepted or refused not for its intrinsic value but only in relation to the person who presents it. This different value given to the content and to the relationship by "healthy" and "sick" families was initially noted by Ruesh and Bateson (1951) and later confirmed by Watzlawick and colleagues:

> ... the more spontaneous and "healthy" a relationship, the more the relationship aspect of communication recedes into the background. Conversely, "sick" relationships are characterized by a constant struggle about the nature of the relationship, with the content aspect of communication becoming less and less important. (Watzlawick, Beavin, & Jackson, 1967, p. 52)

## The Family as a Mind

Consistent with the views of Gregory Bateson (1980), I view the family as a system that has the same complex organization and meets the same structural requirements of *a mind*. Thus, the presenting problems of the family can be seen as a failure to adaptively integrate the different roles and family functions; as a result, dissociative disturbances develop and maintain the presenting problem(s).

## The Hypnotic Process with Families

In this section, I briefly present how the hypnotic process with families develops, based on a general perspective proposed by Jay Haley (1987).

### The Social Phase

In the beginning of the therapeutic encounter, the therapist should not interview the family to elicit information about their symptoms, problems, or complaints. Instead, in this phase, the therapist should focus on obtaining social knowledge about the family in order to explore and identify qualities and resources that can be used in the course of the therapeutic process.

### The Interaction Phase

Before the hypnotic induction, the therapist should understand how the family interacts, if there are dysfunctional patterns, and, if so, what they are. The therapist in this phase observes and activates the family interaction patterns to identify the family connections and disconnections, to select the most appropriate family induction and organize the structure of the therapeutic intervention. In this phase, I begin to explore the symptom or the problem that brought the family into therapy; but, even with this goal in mind, it is useful to maintain a *resource-oriented approach*. So, instead of asking the typical question, "What is the problem?" I ask each family member two questions: (1) "What would you like to change?" and (2) "What would you like to keep the same?" The first question puts a strong emphasis on the future and on the family potentialities. The second one underlines the concept of family strengths.

### The Induction Phase

Before proceeding with the induction, the therapist should create a hypnotic context that will facilitate the participation of the family members in the common experience of trance. Explaining what hypnosis is or clarifying misconceptions about hypnotic trance is useful in this phase. Family members can then be invited to provide their consent to participate in the family hypnotic experience. They are also informed of the option to remain outside of it. So they can participate in session, without entering the trance, or even go back and forth if they choose. At this point, one of the induction techniques described later in this chapter can be adopted.

### The Utilization Phase

Based on the Ericksonian idea of *utilization,* all the material derived from the initial part of the therapy should be utilized to reach the therapeutic goals agreed upon with the couple/family. Resources, potentials, and aspects of family function that they want to keep as well as symptoms and interactive changes or hypnotic phenomena observed in the induction phase can all be utilized to obtain change and overcome family dysfunctional patterns. Specific techniques can be used to *tailor* the therapeutic intervention to the family interaction style and family or individual resistance can be used for therapeutic purposes.

### The Conclusion Phase

The conclusion phase takes place as the therapeutic goals are achieved. Satisfaction with outcome, when shared by all of the family members, is considered a sign of successful treatment, especially when it is accompanied by the significant reduction in or disappearance of the family dysfunctional behaviors.

### Family Disassociation and Integrative Inductions

Here I present five specific examples of *integrative inductions*. Of course, it is important to clarify that each of these examples should *not* be viewed as scripts to be read to families as presented. It is better to think of them as examples of the type of induction a therapist might use with a particular family. This is one of the reasons that it is important to spend some nonhypnotic portion of the session engaged in the social phase, during which the clinician does not interview the family about their symptoms, problems, or complaints but instead explores resources that can inform the therapeutic process, including the induction.

### Family Qualities as the Basis of Family Inductions

To structure and tailor a family induction, a therapist should ask about and identify individual and family qualities that will enforce the therapeutic approach. Practically everything that is not a symptom or a complaint, and is specific of an individual or of a family, can be considered a quality or resource.

### Examples of Individual Qualities

1. *Passions and hobbies* are subjective and idiosyncratic behaviors of each family member.
2. *Desires and projects* indicate the individual's expectations and readiness for change.
3. *More frequent words* help the therapist to learn and use the individual's language.
4. *Key personal concepts* usually indicate implicit motivation for change.

**Examples of Family Qualities**

1. *Open conflicts* are often considered dysfunctional. However, even though hidden conflicts cannot be solved, open conflicts can be negotiated and therefore facilitate systemic change.
2. *Hidden harmony*. Although dysfunctional families exhibit an apparent harmony, or even *pseudomutuality* (Wynne, Rickoff, Day, & Hirsh, 1958), hidden forms of harmony are more profound and sincere, and they should be recognized and preserved by the therapist.
3. Physical *synchronism* brings with itself emotional attunement in the family, and it can be used to increase family cohesion.
4. *Shared imagination* and fantasies are an important part of the family life. Family myths and legends, feelings of guilt, expectations, and loyalties are just a few direct or indirect effects of the shared imagination.

As the number of family potentialities and resources is practically infinite, the examples above are far from complete. However, they draw attention to some of those that may be less frequently considered. As the reader will note, symptoms, problems, and complaints have been excluded from this list of resources. Still, it is important to remember that even these forms of behavior (which are usually viewed as dysfunctional) always contain at least one or more parts that can be considered as a resource (Loriedo & Vella, 1992).

## From Family Disconnections to Integrative Inductions

Family qualities can be used to identify the primary themes and to embed tailored metaphors into the therapeutic inductions. Therapeutic inductions with families have some general goals: to develop each family member's individual qualities, to facilitate cohesion, to open communication channels, and to reestablish integration. The inductions presented here can address all of these goals, although the major emphasis is on their integrative function. Integrative inductions are designed to correct maladaptive connections and disconnections.

## How to Initiate a Family Induction

The family is usually sitting in a semicircle, and the clinician should be seated in a chair from which all the family members are clearly visible. The clinician then asks each family member to provide formal consent to develop hypnosis. After this, the clinician offers a simple statement that precedes each of the inductions and marks the beginning of the process. One example of such a statement could be as follows:

> Since you have all accepted to experience a hypnotic trance together, you can go ahead and get yourself in a comfortable position, and take a deep breath. You can participate with your eyes open or you may close your eyes if you feel more comfortable. I will begin speaking to you and you will listen with your minds and your bodies, and they will be able to respond, without changing your state…

At this point, the integrative induction can begin.

## Integrative Inductions

Integrative inductions can be used with families that do not evidence *harmonic* patterns. Healthy or harmonic families can be defined as well-integrated families where connections and disconnections are flexible and easy to develop based on the needs of the family and its members. Roles and boundaries are well defined but not too rigid or chaotic.

### An Induction for Families with Individual Segregation

In segregating families, one or more family members are caught in the family system and seem to have lost their autonomy. They seem to be segregated inside the family. The other members behave in ways that interfere with their ability to access the external family environment. At the same time, the individual who is segregated appears to be accepting this dysfunctional life style. In these families, one member is segregated from the others in a way that allows the entire system to cover and control intense family conflicts. Having a sacrificing/sacrificed (scapegoat) family member helps the family overcome internal tensions (Ackerman, 1971).

The primary objectives of integrative family inductions with segregating families are to: (1) reduce family internal tension; (2) increase family flexibility; and (3) develop individual autonomy. They are typically used with families where one of the members has been given a diagnosis, such as schizophrenia or depression. (Loriedo & Torti, 2010).

#### *The "Magic Bridge" Induction with Commentary*

**Clinician: A family has been living for a very long time on a beautiful island with nice landscapes and an enchanting**

**sea. On the island, there is everything people could desire to make them happy.**

*[The therapist describes the structure of the family like a beautiful island, which provides both the idea of isolation and the idea of a resourceful place.]*

**Unfortunately, some years ago rival bands began to fight against one another in order to have control over the island.**

*[These families consider the outside world as dangerous and try to protect their members with rigid boundaries that carry with them the risk of segregating the family from other people.]*

**From that moment on, life on the island became difficult and dangerous, tension is always in the air, and there are frequent explosions that create panic and the risk of being involved in a battle and being seriously injured.**

**Living in these unsafe situations makes the inhabitants worried and unhappy. Everyone in the family is preoccupied about the safety of him- or herself and the other family members.**

*[The danger tends to produce a double effect: the need to protect and the desire to escape. Each individual member of the family is caught in the dilemma of whether to stay or go. To abandon the others would be disloyal to the family and to remain will be too dangerous. If the entire family moves away, all the family interests, including their home, will be abandoned and perhaps left to the fury of the guerrilla bands. The induction tends to open the family boundaries, but it should be made in a way that can be acceptable for the family.]*

**One day, one of you (who is silently suffering because of the difficult situation), being in despair, is walking and**

**takes an unusual path. After walking for some minutes, you unexpectedly see a bridge. No one on the island ever talked about a bridge, and until now the inhabitants were always obliged to take a boat to reach the mainland.**

**Was the bridge made recently by the government and without any notification or news? Was it a hallucination or a mirage? Or maybe, a magical bridge was made to create a solution for those who wanted to escape from the unsafe situation of the island. No one knows for sure, but the bridge is there.**

*[A mysterious bridge offers a way out that does not explicitly threaten the family's current structure. It can be just a dream, and a dream cannot be dangerous for family balance. And, after all, a new bridge is a new connection and not necessarily one that is either in- or outside the family.]*

**You remain in front of the bridge for a while considering whether or not to cross it. Would that be considered a betrayal of the family, or rather an opportunity to find a way out, or possibly help for everybody else?**

*[Since no one in the family system is specified, the door to pass over the bridge is open to all, and every family member, even the scapegoat, could be entitled to cross the family boundaries.]*

*[A bridge, whether magical or not, is a two-way resource; you can cross it in both directions. You can go and come back easily. The inhabitants living on an island tend to think in terms of either/or. You are either on the island or on the mainland. A bridge changes the perspective completely: to cross it doesn't mean abandoning the island or the family, or being disloyal. It is just a question of distance. Coming back is easy and comfortable.]*

*[The intense experience outside the boundaries changes both the one(s) who go over the bridge as well as the ones who remain and the island itself. Since all those who went away for a time are returning home, opening the boundaries from now on can appear reassuring and maybe useful.]*

**You stand in the middle of the bridge thinking about what is left on the island but continue to feel a sense of continuity and connection with the family. On the other side, on the mainland, it is already possible to see a different world in front of you; there is a very quiet and peaceful atmosphere, a green-grass meadow, and pleasant music.**

**The sound of the music and smelling the grass seem to create a profound connection between the island and the mainland, an invisible bridge that connects all.**

**The further you go across the bridge, the more the music and the grass smell become intense. At the same time, the quiet and peaceful sensations become more intense. And once on the mainland, these sensations become so intense that you feel the need to let yourself experience them, to feel quiet and peaceful. There has been a long period of suffering and tension on the island. The urge to let yourself rest and relax invites you to lie down on the comfortable grass and close your eyes.**

*[Now the experience becomes more openly hypnotic and includes induction of relaxation, olfactory and visual hallucinations, dreaming, amnesia, and time distortion. If these phenomena are experienced by the family members, we can discover that they have changed their initial point of view. Since it is the mainland that offers these unusual phenomena, to experience them implies having crossed the bridge.]*

It is like sleeping a very deep sleep and dreaming without any need to remember. You can remain like this for all of the time that you need in order to recover from the difficult period you have gone through.

When you wake up, you are not sure how much time you spent laying in the meadow; it could have been minutes, it could have been hours, or it could have been days.

Naturally, you look over the bridge back to the island that you left some time ago. And you become curious, because there are no longer any sounds of explosions or of battles that in the last years were so frequent.

Another surprise is to notice that back on the island there is now a smell of great meadows of green grass. Grass had been disappearing from the island because of the many battles and explosions, and to see it again in large meadows is certainly a great surprise. An even greater surprise is the music; it is all over the island, and it provides a sense of calm and peace.

You are curious about your home back on the island. You walk to it, and when you reach it you discover that the door is open—it has always been closed and locked before—and even inside here there is music.

The other family members are happy to see you again, and they appear quiet and calm too. It looks like the tempest is gone. Worries and unhappiness seem to belong to the past and everybody looks confident about the future.

You ask to yourself, "How is all this possible?"

Did I stay in the mainland for months, and in the meantime one of the bands has overcome the others?

**Have all the warriors been arrested? Or did everybody in the family (and maybe on the island) cross the bridge and learn how to be quiet and calm? Did I dream that the island was unsafe and dangerous, and crossing the bridge awakened me? Or did I simply cross a magical bridge? I am not sure.**

**I only know the bridge is a two-way resource. I can cross it in both directions. And the bridge is still there. It can be crossed back and forth whenever needed.**

*[For a family that has diffuse internal and rigid external boundaries, it is important to accept new connections and a two-way resource that "can be crossed back and forth whenever is needed."]*

**Now each one of you can take a deep breath and open your eyes and see how the other family members have quiet and peaceful expressions in their faces.**

### An Induction for Families with Individual Dissociation

In families with an acceptable internal cohesion, one (or more) family members *may be* treated as if they were not part of the family. The dissociated individual asks for more consideration, but these requests have no real effect on the family behavior. More attention—but certainly not enough—can be gained when the individual develops a symptom, particularly if the symptom has a somatic flavor. The primary dysfunctional family pattern here is one of *emotional or physical neglect*, where the excluded member is treated as if he or she does not belong to the family.

The primary objectives of the induction in this case are to: (1) increase the family interest in and attention paid toward the "patient;" (2) allow the dissociated individual to experience being seen and accepted; and (3) help the family system recognize what they have lost and how important it is to include again the neglected individual among the family resources. The typical presenting problems of the "patient" in such families include somatoform disorders, eating disorders (e.g., bulimia nervosa), and borderline personality disorder.

### *The "Neglected Painting" Induction*

**Clinician: After an intense thunderstorm, the family realizes that the ceiling of one of the rooms in their house has some leaks. The roof probably needs repair, and the family members decide to inspect the attic.**

*[The thunderstorm appears to be the agent of serious damage to the roof of the house. But is it really damaged? This is a typical form of intervention with families, that Mara Selvini Palazzoli, Boscolo, Cecchin, and Prata (1978) called a positive connotation: giving a new and positive frame to an adverse event or to a negative behavior.]*

**The rain has left a damp stain on the ceiling, and in the center of the stain, drops are falling on a large cloth.**

**Whatever is under the cloth could be damaged by the water. It is important to see if it might be something of value, but nobody remembers what is hidden in that neglected part of the house.**

*[Difficult moments can divert the family's attention toward something that, despite its value, has been neglected for a long time.]*

**With a sense of surprise, the family discovers a painting under the cloth, an old and dusty painting. Luckily, the rainwater dripping from the ceiling only ruined a part of the frame, not the canvas. But dust needs to be removed in**

**order to see the painted image. After some days of delicate and careful cleaning, the painting is revealed to be an incredibly beautiful image of people around a fireplace.**

**Although no family member has any memory of such a beautiful picture, and none even knew of its existence, all of them are enchanted by its beauty. Some family members are strongly attracted by the image to the point of spending their time in front of it, like they might sit around and view a real fireplace.**

*[In the beginning, the family's attention is deeply attracted by the material value of the discovered painting, but gradually some other qualities are considered: inspiration, warmth, and togetherness. Other family members, instead, prefer to think about the painting's commercial value. "It is an old painting, maybe it has some value. We could sell it and gain some money, after all the roof needs to be repaired…"]*

**Someone in the family takes the initiative to ask an antique dealer to evaluate the painting, and the response is shocking: the value of the painting is twice as much as the entire family house.**

**The material value of the painting is huge, but slowly the family members continue to discover in the old painting new meanings.**

**The family begins a long discussion about what to do with the money obtained by selling the picture. But a part of the family questions how much better it would be to keep the painting: "After all it is an inspiring picture, we all like it. Watching it is like sitting in front of a real fireplace, a sense of warmth and togetherness comes out of the canvas…"**

**Another says, "It is a part of our history that we do not remember, a connection with our ancestors that we would be crazy to lose..." And another says, "We never talked so much before; in the last few years, before that revealing thunderstorm, we hardly spoke to each other at all. Now the discovery of this painting has resulted in the miracle of reconnecting all of us in endless discussion that is bringing life back into our family. I do not want to go back to that terrible absence of life."**

*[The neglected parts are now becoming essential to reconnect with each other and with their past. They also help to re-evaluate the healthy part of the past (the ancestors), and the dysfunctional one (absence of life). The emotional atmosphere that the discussion creates in the family convinces most of the family members but not all of them. The discovery of neglected values creates conflicts and unbalance in the family: time is needed to adjust to the new emotional climate.]*

**One of the family members proposes to ask the antique dealer to offer her opinion about what to do with the painting; this solution is accepted by all the family.**

*[To restore balance and to overcome conflicts, an expert is needed who can help the family understand the true value of the neglected object, indicating at the same time how value is enhanced by appreciation, care, and protection.]*

**After listening to each family member, the expert says, "You have found a treasure in your house, a neglected treasure you ignored and that was there in your home for many years. Now that you have found it, I understand your willingness to make it part of your life and to enjoy it. From a commercial point of view, I can say that the value of the painting will only increase in time. Better still, it**

**will continue to add financial and emotional richness to the family. So if you want to maintain the painting, I can only offer you a suggestion. Before, you didn't know it was here. Now, it should be treated as we treat all real treasures. You can demonstrate your appreciation by giving it proper care and protection."**

**One member of the family says, "That means we have to take out an insurance policy for the painting." Another one, the family member who usually says very little, responds, "Yes, let's take out an insurance policy. But we should also look to see what other neglected items we might have in the attic or in the cellar, resources that we might have in the family and inside ourselves. And we should take care of and nurture them. Not only when a thunderstorm comes..."**

*[A new family path is traced: from neglect to care, from past to present, from outside to inside, from unexpected values to pursuit of values.]*

### An Induction for Families with Family Dissociation

A family with family dissociation has emotional and physical connections that are very loose; their members appear unable to get closer. Cold and distant relationships create an atmosphere of reciprocal isolation. The primary dysfunctional family pattern is disengagement. Salvador Minuchin (1974) describes those families as "disengaged," with rigid internal boundaries and limited communication.

The objectives of inductions with these families are to: (1) increase a sense of warmth and pleasure; (2) reduce the fear of reciprocal involvement; and (3) restore communication and connections. The typical presenting problems of the "patient" in these families are schizoid personality disorder, obsessive-compulsive disorder, and personality disorders.

*The "Special Concert" Induction*

**Clinician: Each one of you loves music, but the kind of music you love is different. Some might most enjoy classical music and others rock. Maybe some like intimate and soft melodies, and others prefer rhythmic electronic compositions.**

**For some of you, it is better to listen to instrumental music, while others might prefer vocals.**

**Some will be delighted by the Jamaican flavor of reggae music, and others will prefer soothing and relaxing easy listening music. You may like the furious power of metal and others may enjoy listening to the inner calm of new age music.**

*[Disengaged families take advantage of confusion techniques. They have lost their sense of belonging and do not have any clear landmark. Oscillation and uncertainty tend to create disorder and unstable relationships.]*

**Religious music can attract many people, but some people choose gospel or spirituals, and others will be enchanted by Gregorian chanting. And if you like jazz, you may prefer it hot, or cool, or even free, performed by great swing bands or improvised by creative soloists.**

*[Confusion allows these families to reset and start again: this special progressive confusion gives rise to a need for novelty and reassuring closeness.]*

**You may even prefer combinations of styles, like in the acid jazz that combines elements of funk and soul, with**

**electronic music, in a similar way in which fusion can combine jazz and rock with the traditions of world music.**

*[Now, the differences become subtler; they can belong to the same subgroup. It is possible to be different and at the same time to be close.]*

**But you could have noticed sometimes with surprise that a well-defined musical genre can develop in a direction that embraces others that are very different.**

*[Gradually confusion changes and leads to the possibility of combining styles that are very different.]*

**Like Christian rockers, despite their deeply grounded religious feelings, can write and perform with great energy. At the same time, heavy metal players have produced melodious and romantic music.**

*[Finally, on special occasions, different styles become just different expressions of the same style.]*

**I do not expect that all of you enjoy music in the same way or even enjoy all musical genres; neither do I want you to change your musical preferences. On the contrary, it is important that everyone in the family develop his or her own personality. I would like each of you to select a specific kind of music. It could even be a specific and personal piece or song to concentrate on.**

*[The progression is ended, and after this special brain washing the family needs some time to rearrange their point of view. Now the emphasis is on the individuals, with the implicit presupposition that you should be an individual in order to belong.]*

**You may concentrate on listening to that music, and the more you go on, the more you will be able to experience it and feel the music vibrations all over your body.**

*[Family members can now move together with the music.]*

**You can even discover in your body little movements and oscillations that can accompany the music. And this experience of moving together with the music you love gives you a profound sense of freedom and wellbeing.**

*[The music is different for each individual, but they listen to the music and move together. Although each one is free to make a personal choice, the family members now know that all of them are having the same experience at the same time.]*

*[But what is considered more dangerous by the components of these families is intrusion. To avoid intrusive behaviors on the part of others, they prefer to maintain a great emotional distance.]*

**Now I would like to give you a special headset that allows you to listen to the music wherever you go. You can climb a mountain or you can be jogging in a park, walking on a beach, or canoeing on a river. Wherever you go, your special music will be with you, thanks to the special headset I gave you. Your body will continue to move together with the music, and the profound sense of freedom and wellbeing will continue to accompany you wherever you are.**

*[The special headset is the perfect instrument to avoid intrusion since it allows the shared experience of the special concert, without being invaded by the music of others.]*

**And while you walk or run with your special headset that allows you to bring your special music with you, you**

**discover that you are arriving in a special place. It is a wonderful venue and each one of you will find in this special place what you really want to find, and you finally realize that is the special place for a special concert.**

*[The concept of both and is now founded: individual and family are no more mutually exclusive. This is the basis of the complexity theory: opposite positions can be compatible.]*

**For each one of you this will be your concert, thanks to your special headset, but you will see in the same special place all the other family members that are having their special concert too.**

*[The integrative induction is giving to this type of family a very unusual experience of being together in a shared context of emotions and pleasure.]*

**And the surprise is that you maintain your profound sense of freedom and wellbeing, while you listen to your special music. But at the same time, you can see the other family members having the same sense of freedom and wellbeing, moving their body accompanying the music like you do. Sometimes you can see one member of your family moving so close that even a little physical contact is possible. Like in any beautiful concert, each one is feeling intense emotions, but in this special case, a new sense of warmth comes out of sharing the same emotions derived by different stimuli.**

*[To see the others enjoying themselves being there and to be seen by them while you are having a good time is certainly not common in this family.]*

**Now you have experienced the two faces of freedom, the freedom to be yourself and the freedom to be together.**

*[In everyday life, if these experiences happen, they are accompanied by criticism, blaming attitudes, dangerous intrusions, unpleasing emotions.]*

**If you enjoyed the experience, you can continue to explore it: you have your special music, and you have the special headset I gave you.**

**So you take a comfortable position, and take a deep breath, concentrate on the music and you can go every time you want to a new special concert.**

**The place where you can develop more and more the freedom to be yourself and the freedom to be together.**

*[The therapist provides a safe experience like the special concert, not only during the session but also as a posthypnotic suggestion that they can perform at home. This allows them to have individual experiences of the special concert when it is a most suitable. But if the family shows a high level of compliance, the experience made at home of going all together in the same moment to the concert will strongly enforce the therapist's work. In other cases, it could be a goal for future sessions.]*

### An Induction for Families that are Hyper-Connected

Families that are hyper-connected are families who are strongly connected with each other but dissociated from the rest of the world. Individuals are allowed to interact with the other family members, but they do not have permission to develop meaningful external relationships. External attempts to enter the family system are usually gently refused or strongly rejected. The typical dysfunctional family pattern of hyper-connected families is one of enmeshment. Minuchin (1974) describes such families as intensely interwoven and with little space for individual autonomy.

The goals of the integrative induction for enmeshed families are: (1) to reduce reciprocal involvement; (2) encourage exploration of the outside world; and (3) provide and receive permission for individual differentiation and autonomy. The typical presenting problems of the "patient" of such families include psychosomatic disorders, phobias, and eating disorders (anorexia nervosa).

***The "Imaginary Trip" Induction***

**Clinician: Imagine your family sitting together in the dining room and having a discussion about what to do next summer. It is not easy, because of the different opinions, to find a plan that could be considered OK for every family member.**

> *[Beginning with the word imagine is seeding much of what will follow.]*

**But on one point everyone agrees—to go on a beautiful trip all together. But, deciding where to go and how to travel appears a very difficult task.**

> *[Here is clarification that hyper-connected families, despite their closeness, might have serious difficulties in making decisions. They may agree on general principles but became paralyzed when it is time to apply those principles.]*

**So let me ask your permission to offer you a trip that will be completely satisfying for each participant. Will you allow me to offer you this unusual but profoundly satisfying trip? I would like to have a response from those of you who would like to participate in the trip. You can**

**say yes or just move your head affirmatively, now. Thanks to all of you for responding yes.**

*[I consider it very important, particularly in a hyper-connected family, to make a formal request to the entire family from time to time; to obtain every single individual's consent for different therapeutic suggestions.]*

**Are you ready to begin the imaginary trip? An imaginary trip is just imagination, no more than imagination. But let me tell you that the power of imagination goes beyond imagination...**

*[Imagination is an individual quality but can become shared by the entire family. This peculiar aspect can make it an important resource for families because it can respond and adapt to the family's needs; that is, to both belong and to individuate.]*

**One hundred and fifty years ago, a famous French researcher suggested that imagination is much stronger than will and that imagining something can provide us with more success than just wanting something.**

*[Although the official trip has not yet begun, the trip in the family's imagination has started. I am a guide in its multiform aspects.]*

**So an imaginary trip can be more effective than a wanted and well-organized one. And by practicing imagination, you can improve it to the point of making it a part of your personal realty.**

*[On a real trip, visual imagery can prevail over all other senses. In an imagined trip, you can learn to develop not only one form of perception but all of them. Touching, smelling, listening, tasting, and any other physical experience can be activated.*

*Imagination gives to the therapist/guide the possibility to explore an entire world of hypnotic phenomena.]*

**And you can adapt, in your imagination, your perceptions, to your preferred dimensions. So you can have few enemies and many friends. Or you can travel with a speedy airplane, or play tennis in slow motion. You can enjoy sailing in a strong wind or eating a pleasant appetizer on a terrace with a gentle breeze. And you can shorten or expand your time according to your needs: standing in a line can take just a few seconds, while the more pleasant moments of your trip can last for a very long time.**

*[Here I note that they can experience sensations and perceptions as they like.]*

**And you can eat plenty of your favorite food without feeling guilty and without gaining weight. But you can also enjoy little portions, being fully satisfied, knowing how to taste carefully all the little pieces of your meal.**

**And you can adjust the weather to your preferences, having a sunny day but with a mild and pleasant temperature or find the right amount of snow to ski on the mountain. You can hear the right music that will accompany every different moment, and the proper dress for dining or the right equipment for your preferred sport, the right colors for the pictures you are taking, and more comfortable transportation to move from one place to the other.**

*[In an indirect safe and pleasant way, the initial basis for individual autonomy is now set. It is just a fantasy, so it can be accepted by all the other family members, because every one of them is having a similar fantasy.]*

**Finally, you can bring with you the members of the family that you prefer for each different part of the trip. The people with you will adapt to you and will also be able to be flexible from moment to moment. And they will be able to find the right distance, respecting your privacy or giving you the needed amount of warmth and intimacy.**

*[Now is time to give the imaginary trip the meaning of reconnection with others, but the encounter with the other family members too will be adjusted and softened by imagination. The same principle that allowed them to adapt their perceptions of reality, will now allow them to approach only the family parts they like the most.]*

**Now I will give you time to complete your imaginary trip and, when you are ready, you can open your eyes and describe to all of us the places you have visited, the people who were with you and the particular experiences you had during the trip.**

*[After a few minutes, the family members begin to describe their experiences. When all of them have concluded their description, the therapist suggests that they prepare for the second part of the imaginary trip. Before they begin, once again, individual consent to participate to the second part of the induction is asked. Personal consent is asked again, but this time, asking in an open way if they want to participate in their personal imaginary trip, it means building the basis for each one's autonomy already previously set in an indirect way. Further, since all are giving their personal consent, everyone is implicitly giving consent to the others' individual autonomy.]*

**The second part of the imaginary trip will be completed by each one of you alone. Previously, you traveled with those members of your family who could adapt to the specific**

**trip you were on or with those who you considered most appropriate to the experiences you were going through.**

*[Again the principle of both and is emphasized as the best method to have a completely satisfying experience. The imaginary experience that was seeded at the beginning of the first induction.]*

**Now, you will be able once again to use your imagination, but this time there will not be any family members with you: that was your family imaginary trip, now you will have your personal imaginary trip.**

**In order to a have a completely satisfying trip, you should experience both of them.**

**During your personal imaginary trip, not only will you be alone and without any other family members, but you will know that all the other family members will be alone as well on their trips.**

**But since you will be alone and they will be alone, you will be alone but in a shared experience with all the others who will be alone, at the same time as you, on their personal trips. So your personal trip will be a personal experience, but your personal trip, together with their personal trips, will be a shared experience. And the pleasure for your personal experience will add to their pleasure for their personal experience.**

*[As with disengaged families, with the enmeshed ones some part of confusion proves to be useful. But in this case, it should be: (1) soft, (2) progressive and (3) incomplete confusion. In soft confusion, the therapist uses complex statements that, although confounding, maintain a logical structure. This approach is different from the so-called hard confusion, where the logical*

*structure of the therapist's speech is not present. Progressive confusion is a form of confusion that becomes gradually more intense, giving the subjects time to gradually adapt. Incomplete confusion is a confusion technique, without the final suggestion. As described by Erickson, after the subject is confounded "... the culmination is then in a final suggestion permitting a ready and easy response..." (Erickson, 1964, p. 207).]*

**And though they will have their separate personal experience, you will have the shared pleasure of knowing that they will be having their personal pleasure while you will be having your personal pleasure.**

*[Give a one-minute or so pause to allow the family members to get rid of the momentary tension that comes out of the confusion.]*

**Now, I do not want to interfere with your experience and will leave you all the time you need to complete it, to the point of being fully satisfied.**

*[Because hyper-connected families are used to invading each other, a final suggestion after confusion would be felt as an undue intrusion. In these cases, incomplete confusion without any final suggestion will be better accepted.]*

**And this will be the completion of both your family imaginary trip and of your personal imaginary trip.**

**Then you will take a deep breath, take your time, and then open your eyes.**

**When you are completely reoriented, you can describe to the other family members and to me what your trip was like.**

*[Pause until the family members demonstrate with their movements and other nonverbal behaviors they are ready to describe their experience.]*

**Now you can reorient yourself, and as soon as you are ready, you can begin to describe your experience...**

*[A therapist that does not interfere with the subject's experience and leaves them the time to complete it, demonstrating respect for each individual's process of autonomy.]*

### An Induction for Disassociated or Chaotic Families

Chaotic family systems (Olson, 2000) are connected but in illogical ways; transgenerational coalitions in which children are hyper-involved with one parent and disconnected from the other is a frequent configuration. A childish parent asking for a parent in the partner or in a child or a parental child asking for a child/parent are other common configurations. The typical family pattern of disassociated families has been labeled *skewed* by Theodore Lidz (1960) because of their disordered and disharmonic forms of interaction. We can say that all of what should be connected is disconnected and all of what should be disconnected is connected.

The induction objectives for such families are to: (1) facilitate order and structure; (2) reestablish roles and generational hierarchies; and (3) increase a sense of we-ness as well as individual autonomy. The typical problems of the presenting "patient" in such families are members engaging in chaotic behavior, anti-social personality disorders, or drug addiction.

*The "Silent Orchestra" Induction*

**Clinician: You can imagine your family as an orchestra, an orchestra that for many important reasons has not played together for a long time. During all that time, some of you have played solos, some have played in other orchestras, and some have not played at all.**

*[The therapist might introduce here the many reasons he or she knows from the information given by the members that explain why the family orchestra was unable to play together for so long.]*

**In the last few years, everyone had different musical and personal experiences, and now it is hard to predict whether or not you will be able to find again a shared harmony.**

**Now the old impresario calls you one by one and asks if you are available for an important concert that will take place in a few hours; the regular orchestra that was supposed to play tomorrow will not be able to perform because of an airline strike. There are only a few hours to practice before the concert, and the question is will it be possible to be ready so soon?**

*[Chaotic families often need greater effort on the part of the therapist to enter hypnosis, because their attention tends to be more diffused than focused. Doubts and uncertainty are introduced to draw the family attention in such a way that entering in hypnosis is the only way to find an answer.]*

**Now is the moment of the first rehearsal, all the instruments are close to you, and the director is in the orchestra pit, waiting for all the players to begin to test their instruments. But unexpectedly none of the players**

**moves or touches the instruments; all of them remain immobile and silent.**

*[For the same reason, indirect suggestions of immobility and silence are used.]*

**A silent orchestra with all the players and the instruments in their places induces a tremendous sense of expectation, particularly in the director, who never saw such a completely paralyzed orchestra, but there is not much time to lose; the concert is tomorrow and it is essential to begin to practice immediately.**

*[Expectation is another key concept to establish an atmosphere of interest and concentration.]*

**After trying different commands that do not get any response from the orchestra members, the director doesn't understand what is happening and begins to worry. Possible conclusions are that the players prefer not to play at all since they are afraid of failing, or that each one of them is waiting for someone to begin to play to avoid the responsibility of being the first to play. Or maybe they are waiting for some special directive.**

*[For disassociated families to have three different explanations is better than just one. They rarely agree on one idea but may find it useful to accept different explanations.]*

**At this point, although the director is also afraid of failure, there is no doubt that, given his or her position, he or she is the one that should first take the responsibility and the most risk.**

*[To know that someone else will take on the responsibility of possible failure can be relieving.]*

**But how to best take on this responsibility, while all the orchestra is immobile and silent?**

*[Behavioral passivity is possible, but nonverbal language never stops. An orchestra director should know how to facilitate reciprocal tuning among all of the instruments; this is usually possible by connecting the different sounds of the musical instruments.]*

**Unfortunately, at this point, it does not appear possible for the musical instruments to be played by the musicians. So the director decides to initiate a form of special attuning, trying to connect the players in an unusual way. The directors says, "Close your eyes, if you want, and pay attention to your body. You will realize you are breathing and you can feel the rhythm of your breathing."**

*[Each one's body becomes an instrument that can be played, as such, in every day of the individual's life. And the attempt here is to connect each individual body to form a unique and well-functioning family body.]*

**You can also realize that while breathing, you are moving some parts of your body. Breathing and moving.**

**But if you pay even more attention, you can feel the breathing and movements of the people who are close to you. And I'm sure that as soon as you feel the others' breathing and moving you will discover that your body gradually synchronizes with the other bodies.**

*[Synchronization is the first goal to be reached. As we know, hypnosis has the capacity to increase the family's synchronic behaviors, so this intervention is facilitated by spontaneous phenomena. Soon all the bodies in the room will be synchronized and attuned, the breathing sound will become a shared unified*

*sound, and the movements' rhythm will become like a unique harmonic dance. It is more difficult to obtain in a disorganized family an acceptance of well-defined roles and rules. Even the metaphor of one instrument's part of an entire piece, with all of the pauses and accents, may not be sufficient to obtain the desired effect.]*

**You all are finding a natural rhythm that allows you to play your bodies like a well-tuned orchestra.**

**Something is missing, because in an orchestra each musician should have a role that is different from the others.**

**And more: there are moments in which all the instruments play together and moments in which only one or a few of them play; there are pauses and there are accents. But even if you begin to be well synchronized, before all the rest there is a musical score with its rhythms that you have to follow.**

*[Only shared embodied experiences can obtain from very resistant families a meaningful change that can be maintained in the memory of the entire family mind (in this case, following Bateson's ideas, the word "mind" is intended to include the body).]*

**This will give you the structure of the harmony, and you all will know what each one of you has to do, respecting your part, and others' parts.**

**With perfect timing and giving your contribution to the complexity of the melody.**

**You have your musical parts in front of you, and you can read them. But in the meantime, we will improve the way we play our bodies' symphony.**

**But since I would like to direct this bodies' concert, I will begin to direct you with my body.**

*[At this point, therapist and director become the same thing and they decide to be unified and to assume the responsibility for change in their person.]*

**Now my feet are on the floor, and the left foot will soon begin to beat in order to give the rhythm to the ones of you that are at my left.**

*[The therapist is not only the one who activates change, but also the one who should find change in him- or herself first. I think this is always the best way to be in tune and produce change in the others (see Whitaker, 1990). The therapist/director begins to beat on the floor with the left foot. Shortly after some family members sitting on the left begin to move rhythmically, and others join a little later, using different parts of their body, clapping hands, beating on the floor, or tapping any surface with one hand. Family members are now able to play their bodies and to play as if they were a unique body.]*

**Now I will tap with my right hand giving the rhythm to the right part of the family. And from now on, the right of the family will respond to my hand and the left to my foot. Sometimes you will have to play separately and sometimes all together.**

*[Very soon, the right part of the family responds with its body sounds attuned to the director's rhythm. Then again the left responds. After a few minutes, the entire silent bodies' orchestra demonstrates a profound physical synchronization even with points and counterpoints and ensembles. So the director concludes. It can be surprising how a group of people, even with little or no musical education, can learn to play in a short time an embodied symphony. But it is not that surprising that*

*hypnosis with families can reawaken innate mechanisms and early learning experiences.]*

**Now you are able to be synchronized and, at the same moment, to follow a part. This tells me that you for sure can play.**

**So as soon as you are ready, open your eyes, look around yourself, go to your instruments, be aware of your part score, give to your body the time to be in tune with the others, wait for my sign, and then begin to play...**

*[The child-parent emotional attunement that takes place in the first two months of life is one of our earliest and deepest learning (Stern, 2002). As in music, family hypnosis is just "Exploiting the ability of human beings to interact rhythmically and expressively" (Trevarthen, 1997).]*

### Summary and Conclusions

We can say that if we consider a family to be a distinct system or, better yet, like a mind, based on the great Gregory Bateson's views, the use of hypnosis can be extremely useful for a number of families' dysfunctional patterns. It is particularly useful to describe these dysfunctions in terms of the dissociative processes that often develop in dysfunctional families and to intervene with specific integrative inductions. From both a theoretical and a clinical perspective, it is interesting to note that hypnosis has been viewed for a long time as a dissociative approach. In fact, hypnosis can also be used as an *associative* intervention that can be used to reestablish synchronization and emotional attunement both in the individual and in the family mind.

## References

Ackerman, N. W. (1971). Prejudicial scapegoating and neutralizing forces in the family group with special reference to the role of the family healer. In J. G. Howells (Ed.), *Theory and practice of family psychiatry* (pp. 626-634). New York, NY: Brunner/Mazel.

Bateson, G. (1980). *Mind and nature: A necessary unity*. New York, NY: Bantam.

Birdwistell, R. L. (1970). *Kinesics and context: Essays on body motion communication*. Philadelphia, PA: University of Pennsylvania Press.

Erickson, M. H. (1964). The confusion technique in hypnosis: A hypnotic technique in resistant patients. *American Journal of Clinical Hypnosis, 6*, 183-207.

Haley, J. (1987). *Problem-solving therapy*. San Francisco, CA: Jossey-Bass.

Kendon, A. (1979). Movement coordination in social interaction. In S. Weitz (Ed.), *Nonverbal communication: Readings with commentary*. New York: NY: Oxford University Press.

Lidz, T., Cornelison, A. R., Fleck, S., & Terry, D. (1960). Schism and skew in the families of schizophrenics, in N. W. Bell & E. F. Vogel (Eds.), *A modern introduction to the family* (pp. 650-662). Glencoe, IL: Free Press.

Loriedo, C. (2008). Systemic trances: Using hypnosis in family therapy. *American Association for Marriage and Family Therapy, Family Therapy Magazine, 7*, 27-30.

Loriedo, C., & Torti, M. C. (2010). Systemic hypnosis with depressed individuals and their families. *International Journal of Clinical and Experimental Hypnosis, 58*, 222-246.

Loriedo, C., & Vella, G. (1992). *Paradox and the family system*. New York, NY: Brunner/Mazel.

Minuchin, S. (1974). *Families and family therapy*. Cambridge, MA: Harvard University Press.

Olson, D. (2000). Circumplex model of marital and family systems. *Journal of Family Therapy, 22, 144–167.*

Ruesch, J., & Bateson, G. (1951). *Communication: The social matrix of psychiatry*. New York, NY: W. W. Norton.

Scheflen, A. E. (1973). *Communicational structure: Analysis of a psychotherapy transaction*. Bloomington, IN: Indiana University Press.

Selvini Palazzoli, M., Boscolo, L., Cecchin, G., & Prata, G. (1978). *Paradox and counterparadox: A new model in the therapy of the family in schizophrenic transaction*. New York, NY: Jason Aronson.

Stern, D. (2001). Face-to-face play: Its temporal structure as predictor of socioaffective development. *Monographs of the Society for Research in Child Development, 66,* 144-149

Trevarthen, C. (1997). Music and Infant Interaction. *Nordisk Tidsskrift for Musikkterapi, 6,* 61-65.

Watzlawick, P., Beavin, J. B., & Jackson, D. D. (1967). *Pragmatics of human communication: A study of interactional patterns, pathologies and paradoxes*. Norton: New York.

Whitaker, C. A. (1989). *Midnight musings of a family therapist*. New York, NY: W. W. Norton.

Wynne, L. C., Rickoff, I. M., Day, J., & Hirsh, S. I. (1958). Pseudomutuality in the family relations of schizophrenics, *Psychiatry, 21,* 205-220.

# CHAPTER 10

# A Hypnotic Induction for Pain Management

**Mark P. Jensen**

*Mark P. Jensen is a Professor and Vice Chair for Research in the Department of Rehabilitation Medicine at the University of Washington in Seattle, USA. He is internationally recognized for his work in developing and evaluating innovative treatments for chronic pain. He has been funded by the National Institutes of Health and other funding agencies in this work and has published extensively (over 450 articles and book chapters) on the topics of pain assessment and treatment.*

*His book on the use of hypnosis for chronic pain management (*Hypnosis for Chronic Pain Management*, published by Oxford University Press; German title,* Hypnose bei chronischem Schmerz: Ein Behandlungsmanual*, published by Carl-Auer) won the 2011 Society of Clinical and Experimental Hypnosis Arthur Shapiro Award for Best Book on Hypnosis. He travels extensively to present his research findings and to teach clinicians effective and empirically supported strategies for helping their clients and patients better manage pain and its effects on their lives. The induction presented here has many of the elements that he typically includes when he begins a formal hypnotic session,* *including those that he has found to be particularly helpful when working with individuals with chronic pain.*

* * *

Given the evidence that inductions increase responsivity to hypnotic suggestions (Derbyshire, Whalley, & Oakley, 2009; Derbyshire, Whalley, Stenger, & Oakley, 2004), even if the increase in responsivity is only "modest" on average (see Chapter 1, this volume), an induction should almost always be a part of the hypnosis session. Some patients, however, may require little more than an, "Okay, go ahead and allow yourself to enter a deep trance, and when you are ready, allow the head to nod" (or, "… the right index finger to raise"). Others may need 10 minutes or longer to be prepared to respond to the therapeutic suggestions. In addition, patients should be debriefed after the session regarding their response to the entire session, including the induction. Their ongoing feedback is useful for determining if they might respond more to inductions that are longer or shorter as well as for identifying the specific language that is most appropriate and useful to them (e.g., whether the induction should focus more or less on visual versus sensory experiences).

It is also useful to know that there are times of the day when people are more or less likely to respond to hypnotic suggestions (Green, Smith, & Kromer, 2015). While the reasons for this observation are not entirely clear, one possible explanation is related to the fact that the times of day when people are more responsive to hypnotic suggestions are also the times of day when they tend to evidence more slow wave—in particular, theta—brain oscillations (Jensen, 2016). More slow wave brain oscillations may make it easier for individuals to perform the tasks required to respond to many common hypnotic suggestions, including suggestions to alter one's sensory experience and change one's point of view towards past events (Jensen et al., 2015). Thus, anything that contributes to more slow wave activity for any particular person—focusing one's attention, listening to a clinician speaking rhythmically, or even suggestions to experience a "sleep-like" state, since more slow wave activity is present during sleep—could potentially enhance or deepen the hypnotic experience, and ultimately help the client become more responsive to the clinical suggestions that follow.

I have found two inductions to be particularly useful when working with patients with chronic pain: a relaxation and a favorite place induction. There are a number of reasons that the relaxation induction is useful in this context. First, feeling more relaxed in response to suggestions for relaxation is "easy" for many (but of course, not all) patients. Many people have experienced a sense of physical relaxation at some point in their lives and can recall that experience. Given this familiarity with a relaxed state, many patients can experience success with this induction, and this success can contribute to increased self-efficacy and foster a positive response set, which then further increases the chances of responding to the clinical suggestions. Second, the experience of deep relaxation tends to be inconsistent with the experience of pain; in particular, the pain associated with musculoskeletal pain conditions. For this reason, some investigators have speculated that relaxation inductions may be more effective than active-alert inductions for increasing responsivity to analgesia suggestions, although inductions that contain suggestions for relaxation are not necessarily any more effective than active-alert inductions for increasing responsivity to other suggestions (Terhune & Cardeña, 2016). Therefore, individuals with chronic pain often experience an increased sense of physical comfort following a relaxation induction alone, which can give them an immediate positive experience. This also contributes to a positive response set and subsequently to a positive response to the clinical suggestions. Third, perceived muscle tension is a symptom of anxiety disorders. Thus, as patients experience a greater sense of physical relaxation, they often also experience a pleasant sense of calm. Clinicians can utilize these common responses and make them a part of the induction, and then link these to a therapeutic response (e.g., "As you feel more relaxed, a growing sense of calm may come over you, allowing you to focus even more on my voice… and those suggestions appropriate for your comfort and well-being…").

Although most people experience relaxation as comfortable and enjoyable, a small minority of individuals do not enjoy the experience of feeling relaxed. Some are uncomfortable with this experience because they associate it with feeling "out of control." Others report a physical sense of "falling" when they feel relaxed (which is one reason to mention "the strong support of the chair below you…" during a relaxation induction, see below). Still others with certain chronic musculoskeletal pain problems report an increase in pain as they experience areas of their body relaxing. While the reasons for this (rare) increase in pain associated with relaxation suggestions are not entirely clear, one possible explanation is that brain activity that is linked to keeping a body area tense may also involve the inhibition of nociception. Given the large number of hypnotic inductions available—including many of those described in this book—it is not necessary or advisable to continue to use any induction that is uncomfortable for a patient. In this case, the clinician can simply move on to another induction, as appropriate. Each induction should ultimately be tailored to be the most effective for the particular patient.

Two of the most useful and related capabilities of the human brain are (1) its ability to shift focus (which effectively inhibits our response to the input that is not the focus of attention) and (2) its ability to dissociate. These built-in capabilities are particularly useful for managing uncomfortable sensations. Most patients with chronic pain can benefit from encouragement to build on these natural abilities.

Patients for whom particular care is needed with respect to considering dissociation suggestions as a component of the induction include patients with a history of trauma and those with dissociative disorders. The former group of patients may be at risk for re-experiencing or recalling traumatic events when invited to have dissociative experiences. Thus, clinicians should be very careful to avoid suggestions during the induction for such patients to experience dissociation (e.g., "… you may feel so relaxed that parts of the body seem to disappear…," referring to body sites as "the" arm or leg instead of "your" arm or leg, inviting them to experience themselves as floating above "that body" during the induction), until they know the patient well and how they might respond to such suggestions. However, for patients who are not at risk for adverse responses to dissociation, I often include suggestions for dissociation, because encouraging this natural ability often increases overall comfort and therefore gives clients a greater sense of control over uncomfortable sensations. The reader will notice a number of places in the induction script that follows that include suggestions for dissociative experiences.

In addition to often using suggestions for relaxation as a component of the induction, I also often include a suggestion that the client experience themselves in a favorite place. There are a number of reasons that this is useful when working with individuals with chronic pain. First, it is always possible to include a body of water in the imagery, and this body of water can be incorporated into clinical suggestions for comfort and healing by inviting the patient at some point to place the body part(s) that is(are) sometimes uncomfortable into the "healing water" (unless, of course, the patient has a water phobia) (Jensen, 2011). Clients whose favorite place is a beach have a number of options for water, including the sea, a stream flowing into the sea, or a pool or tub of water on the beach. Clients whose favorite place is a mountain meadow might experience a stream or lake. If the favorite place is a room, a tub of water (that is "just the right temperature") could be in the room.

Another benefit of using a favorite place as a component of the induction is the fact that the client can be invited to experience the place using all of their senses—what they see, what they feel, what they smell, what they hear, and what they taste. This can help to make their experience more real because they are able to use their preferred sense—not everyone's preferred sense is vision. Related to this, and as already mentioned, there is evidence that hypnosis and hypnotic inductions are associated with increases in slow wave activity, particularly theta, and research indicates that theta activity is required to recall events (Jensen, Adachi, & Hakimian, 2015). Thus, the process of recalling and experiencing an image, taste, smell, feeling, or sound may itself facilitate theta activity, and therefore potentially deepen the hypnotic experience.

Finally, I now commonly use age progression as a component of hypnosis treatment to facilitate hope and give the client (and his or her unconscious) goals to work towards (Jensen, 2011; Jensen et al., 2011; Torem, 1992). One component of this is to invite the client to observe a future version of themselves who has achieved the therapeutic goal, experience themselves as *being* that future version of themselves, and then returning to their current selves while bringing back with them the experience of having achieved their goal and with it the knowledge and confidence that will help them to reach the goal. Already being in a favorite place following the induction provides the client with a space for this work to happen.

### Relaxation and Favorite Place Induction with Commentary

**Clinician: Go ahead and allow yourself to get into a comfortable position; as comfortable as you would like...**

*[Use of permissive language throughout enhances patient control and self-efficacy.]*

**and know that you can change your position or shift at any time... and still remain relaxed and focused.**

*[Patients new to hypnosis might believe that they need to keep still to respond well. This suggestion helps address this potential concern.]*

**When you are ready... ready to experience greater comfort and control... go ahead and allow yourself to take a nice, deep, refreshing breath... that's right... and hold it... hold**

**it for a moment… and let it go. And let yourself notice how good that feels…**

*[Therapeutic bind linking taking a deep breath to responding to suggestions. Also, frequent use of the word "comfort" throughout. Notice that the word "pain" is not used. The goal here is to build and strengthen activity in the brain's focus on comfort.]*

**And now… allow the whole body to relax. Allow all of your muscles to go limp… to relax… to let go… [*wait about three seconds*].**

**And then allow different muscle groups to relax even more. Starting with the right hand… Imagine that all the muscles and tendons in the right hand are relaxing… and as the right hand relaxes…**

**being aware of any sensations that let you know that the hand feels more relaxed… perhaps a sense of warmth, or of heaviness, perhaps some other interesting and comfortable sensation, whatever sensation that lets you know that the right hand is becoming more and more relaxed… limp, heavy, warm and comfortable.**

*[The patient will almost always be able to feel some sensations. Here the clinician suggests that those sensations "mean" comfort. The language is permissive; we are not telling the patient which comfortable sensations they will feel—just suggesting that they are a sign of relaxation.]*

**And now allow that relaxation to spread… up, up into the wrist… the forearm… the elbow… and upper arm. The whole arm becoming more and more relaxed, relaxed and heavy and comfortable. All the tension draining away, as the arm feels heavier, and heavier, almost as if it were**

**made of lead. Or perhaps it might be feeling lighter and lighter. Or even both at the same time. I don't know exactly what sensations of relaxation and comfort you are noticing, and it really does not matter, as long as you experience greater comfort... greater relaxation.**

**And as the body relaxes, so too can the mind relax... experiencing a sense of deep calm. And yet the mind can also stay focused. Focused on my voice... always back to my voice, and those suggestions that are appropriate for your comfort and well-being.**

*[Suggestions to link the increased sense of relaxation that almost all patients will be experiencing at this point to emotional calm and increased focus (hypothesized to facilitate more slow wave activity and a deeper hypnotic state).]*

**And now... allow your awareness to move to your left hand... Imagine how the left hand is becoming limp, heavy, and relaxed... more and more relaxed, heavier and heavier... All the tension just draining away...**

**Letting yourself be aware of any sensation that lets you know that the left hand is relaxing... a warmth, a heaviness, any sensation that lets you know that the left hand is becoming more, and more relaxed...**

**And now allow the relaxation to spread. Up the wrist... forearm... through the elbow, and into the upper arm. So very relaxed, heavy, and comfortable... the whole left arm relaxing, heavier and heavier, or lighter and lighter. More, and more comfortable.**

**And as this process continues, as you continue to allow both of the arms to feel more and more relaxed, you can be aware that the relaxation continues to spread... into the**

**shoulders. All the muscles in the shoulders letting go, relaxing, feeling the support of the chair/bed, sinking into the chair/bed...**

**letting yourself be supported by the strong chair/bed... all the tension draining out of the shoulders ... Feeling so relaxed, heavy, and ... more and more relaxed...**

*[The suggestion for feeling "supported by the strong chair/bed" is for the minority of patients who might experience a sense of falling during the relaxation induction. The word also seeds the idea of the situation being one of "support" which can increase therapeutic alliance.]*

**and the relaxation continues to spread... into the neck. All the muscles and tendons of the neck letting go, one by one. Just allowing the head to rest, being aware of the sensations that let you know that the neck is relaxing, more and more, as you feel more and more comfortable, more and more at ease.**

**The whole body becoming relaxed, very, very relaxed, relaxed... heavy, calm and peaceful... allowing the feelings of comfortable relaxation to spread up around the ears... the scalp... letting all the tension drain away, the muscles around the eyes letting go, relaxing, as do the muscles in the face... the jaw... limp, relaxed, comfortable, and at peace... as relaxed as you have ever been... it feels so good to take a vacation from stress... and the relaxation continues, down the back... into the chest... the stomach... and the pelvis.**

**And then down into the legs... first, the right leg, feeling so very heavy... comfortable... all the tension draining out... limp, heavy, and comfortable. Feeling the support of the chair/bed, the right leg feeling heavier, heavier, and**

**heavier... and so comfortable. And then the left leg... all the tension draining out of the left leg, to be replaced by comfort... a heavy, pleasant, comfortable, and deep relaxation.**

**The whole body relaxing... And when it feels like you are as relaxed as you can be, you can allow yourself to relax *even more,* becoming even *more* relaxed... *more* comfortable, without a care in the world... The whole body relaxed, and comfortable... so relaxed, in fact, that you might even lose awareness of sensations from some parts of the body, almost as if parts of the body were disappearing as they become more comfortable...**

**And you might even find that you experience yourself as a point of consciousness, without any body at all, just floating comfortably and safely in space.**

*[Suggestion for a dissociative experience. Avoid this for patients with a history of dissociative disorder or trauma, until you know the patient well and have determined that such a suggestion might be helpful to them as a part of getting more control over dissociative experiences.]*

**And as you are in space, knowing that you are in space... the body is relaxed and comfortable... resting... healing... strengthening its immune system... you may find yourself moving towards a favorite place.**

*[Can begin to make therapeutic suggestions during the induction, and hint at or "seed" ideas for the primary therapeutic suggestions that will follow.]*

**I do not know where you will find yourself today. It might be a place that you often go... a place of beauty... and**

**comfort... where you can feel as safe as you ever feel... a vacation...**

*[Some patients, in particular those who have a history of trauma, might rarely feel safe. So a suggestion to "feel as safe as you ever feel" is often more useful than a suggestion to feel "safe."]*

**Perhaps it is outside, or if it is inside, you might be able to see outside. You might be able to see the sky. It is a beautiful blue... an intense blue... as blue as you have ever seen...**

*[As the session might be recorded for the patient to listen to on multiple occasions later, it is important to be permissive (i.e., avoid suggesting a specific place), so that recording will have relevance no matter where the patient chooses to go.]*

**And perhaps there are clouds floating... big fluffy white clouds... just floating there so easily and comfortably... enjoying the moment...**

**And the temperature is... just right. Perhaps you can feel the air against your skin... perhaps is it comfortably warm... or comfortably cool... so very comfortable... just as you like it.**

**Looking around... you see beauty... maybe there are plants... the leaves might be very very green... an intense deep comfortable green. Perhaps you see flowers... so very beautiful... the colors intense... somehow absorbing and yet calming.**

**And you can smell the smells that you associate with this beautiful place... and comfort... a sense that you can really be yourself... and just... feel good.**

**And you might now notice the sounds... perhaps you can hear water... so very calming... steady... If it is pleasant,**

**you might hear a bird or birds in the distance... or even a breeze, blowing through the trees...**

**And now, you can see the water. A stream/pool/tub of comfortable, healing water.**

*[The healing water is available for making suggestions (if needed and appropriate) for specific body parts to feel more comfortable and/or or for healing effects (given the evidence that hypnosis can enhance healing; Ginandes, Brooks, Sando, Jones, & Aker, 2003; Ginandes & Rosenthal, 1999).]*

**And a part of you can continue to enjoy all of the benefits of this place. The sense of comfortable calm... a sense of peace... of beauty... a sense of control... because you have created this space just for you... you are in control... and as you enjoy this experience, another part of you can easily hear my voice, always back to my voice, and respond to those suggestions—and only those suggestions—that are appropriate for your comfort and well-being.**

**You might be noticing...**

*[Insert suggestions here, including any posthypnotic suggestions.]*

**And as you absorb and allow those suggestions that you found most helpful to sink in and have their beneficial effects, you might find yourself again floating... floating comfortably in space. Looking down on that body that has been relaxing comfortably this whole time. Noticing perhaps the relaxed expression on his/her face. Being aware that the body is rested. Energized. And letting yourself move back into that body. Feeling how relaxed it is. Feeling perhaps a sense of energy... a sense of strength. Starting to feel ready to come back, and bring back with**

**you any benefits that you have created for yourself during this experience.**

*[Alerting.]*

**In little while, I am going to be quiet. And when I am, you can choose to come back to the here when you are ready. Perhaps signaling that you are ready by allowing the eyes to open. Feeling comfortable, calm, refreshed. Taking all of the time you need.**

*[Permissive language to "come back" as they wish, keeping in mind that the session is likely being recorded and listened to again.]*

**References**

Derbyshire, S. W., Whalley, M. G., & Oakley, D. A. (2009). Fibromyalgia pain and its modulation by hypnotic and non-hypnotic suggestion: An fMRI analysis. *European Journal of Pain, 13*, 542-550.

Derbyshire, S. W., Whalley, M. G., Stenger, V. A., & Oakley, D. A. (2004). Cerebral activation during hypnotically induced and imagined pain. *Neuroimage, 23*, 392-401.

Ginandes, C., Brooks, P., Sando, W., Jones, C., & Aker, J. (2003). Can medical hypnosis accelerate post-surgical wound healing? Results of a clinical trial. *American Journal of Clinical Hypnosis, 45*, 333-351.

Ginandes, C. S., & Rosenthal, D. J. (1999). Using hypnosis to accelerate the healing of bone fractures: A randomized controlled pilot study. *Alternative Therapies in Health and Medicine, 5*, 67-75

Green, J. P., Smith, R. J., & Kromer, M. (2015). Diurnal variations in hypnotic responsiveness: Is there an optimal time to be hypnotized? *International Journal of Clinical and Experimental Hypnosis, 63*, 171-181.

Jensen, M. P. (2011). *Hypnosis for chronic pain management: Therapist guide.* New York, NY: Oxford University Press.

Jensen, M. P. (2016). Brain oscillations and diurnal variations in hypnotic responsiveness—A commentary on "Diurnal variations in hypnotic responsiveness: Is there an optimal time to be hypnotized?". *International Journal of Clinical and Experimental Hypnosis, 64,* 137-145.

Jensen, M. P., Adachi, T., & Hakimian, S. (2015). Brain oscillations, hypnosis, and hypnotizability. *American Journal of Clinical Hypnosis, 57,* 230-253.

Jensen, M. P., Adachi, T., Tomé-Pires, C., Lee, J., Osman, Z. J., & Miró, J. (2015). Mechanisms of hypnosis: Toward the development of a biopsychosocial model. *International Journal of Clinical and Experimental Hypnosis, 63,* 34-75.

Jensen, M. P., Ehde, D. M., Gertz, K. J., Stoelb, B. L., Dillworth, T. M., Hirsh, A. T., . . . Kraft, G. H. (2011). Effects of self-hypnosis training and cognitive restructuring on daily pain intensity and catastrophizing in individuals with multiple sclerosis and chronic pain. *International Journal of Clinical and Experimental Hypnosis, 59,* 45-63.

Terhune, D. B., & Cardeña, E. (2016). Nuances and uncertainties regarding hypnotic inductions: Toward a theoretically informed praxis. *American Journal of Clinical Hypnosis, 59,* 155-174.

Torem, M. S. (1992). "Back from the future": A powerful age-progression technique. *American Journal of Clinical Hypnosis, 35,* 81-88.

**For Further Reading...**

Jensen, M. P. (2009). Hypnosis for chronic pain management: A new hope. *Pain, 146,* 235-237.

Jensen, M. P. (2011). *Hypnosis for chronic pain management: Therapist guide*. New York, NY: Oxford University Press.

Jensen, M. P. (2011). *Hypnosis for chronic pain management: Workbook*. New York, NY: Oxford University Press.

Jensen, M. P. (2016). Pain management—Chronic pain. In G. R. Elkins (Ed.), *Handbook of medical and psychological hypnosis: Foundations, applications, and professional issues* (pp. 341-360). New York, NY: Springer.

Jensen, M. P. (2008). The neurophysiology of pain perception and hypnotic analgesia: Implications for clinical practice. *American Journal of Clinical Hypnosis, 51*, 123-148.

Jensen, M. P., Barber, J., Romano, J. M., Hanley, M. A., Raichle, K. A., Molton, I. R., Engel, J. M., Osborne, T. L., Stoelb, B. L., Cardenas, D. D., & Patterson, D. R. (2009). Effects of self-hypnosis training and EMG biofeedback relaxation training on chronic pain in persons with spinal cord injury. *International Journal of Clinical and Experimental Hypnosis, 57*, 239-268.

Jensen, M. P., Barber, J., Romano, J. M., Molton, I. R., Raichle, K. A., Osborne, T. L., Engel, J. M., Stoelb, B. L., Kraft, G. H., & Patterson, D. R. (2009). A comparison of self-hypnosis versus progressive muscle relaxation in patients with multiple sclerosis and chronic pain. *International Journal of Clinical and Experimental Hypnosis, 57*, 198-221.

Jensen, M. P., Gralow, J. R., Braden, A., Gertz, K. J., Fann, J. R., & Syrjala, K. L. (2012). Hypnosis for symptom management in women with breast cancer: A pilot study. *International Journal of Clinical and Experimental Hypnosis, 60*, 135-159.

Mendoza, M. E., Capafons, A., Gralow, J. R., Syrjala, K. L., Suarez-Rodriguez, J. M., Fann, J. R., & Jensen, M. P. (in press). Randomized controlled trial of the Valencia Model of Waking Hypnosis plus CBT for pain, fatigue, and sleep management in patients with cancer and cancer survivors. *Psycho-Oncology*.

Tan, G., Fukui, T., Jensen, M. P., Thornby, J., & Waldman, K. L. (2010). Hypnosis treatment for chronic low back pain. *International Journal of Clinical and Experimental Hypnosis, 58*, 53-68

Tan, G., Rintala, D. H., Jensen, M. P., Fukui, T., Smith, D., & Williams, W. (2015). A randomized controlled trial of hypnosis compared with biofeedback for adults with chronic low back pain. *European Journal of Pain, 19*, 271-280.

# CHAPTER 11

## Training in Self-Hypnosis as a First Induction

**Bernhard Trenkle**

*Bernhard Trenkle first became interested in clinical hypnosis after he heard a lecture on family therapy over 40 years ago by Helm Stierlin, a professor at the University of Heidelberg. Professor Stierlin described the therapeutic approach of Jay Haley and how Haley was influenced by Milton Erickson. Trenkle began to read Erickson's works and became fascinated with Erickson's use of storytelling, reframing, and utilization for helping clients make rapid and lasting changes. In January 1979, he had his first direct experience with hypnosis during a workshop facilitated by Jeffrey Zeig, and Trenkle's interest in hypnosis deepened.*

*Together with a close colleague, Gunther Schmidt, Trenkle began organizing seminars and workshops in Germany, inviting luminaries such as Jeffrey Zeig, Stephen Lankton, and Stephen Gilligan to facilitate. Over time, Trenkle's interest and experience with hypnosis grew and he soon began teaching and facilitating workshops himself. He has written extensively on hypnotic approaches over the years (e.g., Holtz, Mrochen, Nemetschek, & Trenkle, 2007; Mrochen, Holtz & Trenkle, 1993; Trenkle, 1986, 1988, 1994, 1997, 2008) and is particularly well known for his effective use of humor to communicate complex concepts of hypnosis and psychotherapy (e.g., Trenkle, 2001, 2007).*

* * *

I developed my first ideas about using self-hypnosis training as first trance induction in the context of therapy with a client who had frequently been mistreated in his childhood. Thus, it was understandable that he struggled with hypnosis or relaxation and that he repeatedly stopped the inductions with a feeling of unease.

The technique of first teaching self-hypnosis and then slowly shifting to a safe hetero-hypnotic experience is also helpful with clients who need to be in a one-up position. This was often the case in the 1980s when I worked in the Department of Speech Pathology's university clinic in Heidelberg. The highly experienced teachers, priests, and university professors with psychogenic voice disorders that I treated often had a lot of problems with letting go into a state of deep relaxation. They often saw themselves as needing biomedical treatment only and not treatment with a psychologist. They regularly declared, "My *voice* has a problem; *I* do not have problems. Why should I see a psychologist?"

Teaching them self-hypnosis or deep relaxation techniques first in the way described here, helped them to feel increasingly comfortable in being in a hetero-hypnotic trance state. In addition, at about this same time, I was looking for a story that reflected the resistance associated with seeing a psychologist that resolved into a feeling of letting go and acceptance. I found the story of a lion who was afraid seeing his face in a pool of water (Shah, 1978) and thought that it was perfect for this.

### The Original Story of the Lion

Once upon a time, a lion lived in a desert through which the wind was constantly blowing. As a result, the water in the waterholes he usually drank from was never calm and smooth; the wind was rippling the surface and nothing could be reflected by the water.

One day, the lion walked into a forest, where he hunted and played until he felt rather tired and thirsty. Searching for water he finally reached a pond containing the coolest (most delightful and pleasant) water you could think of. Lions, like other wild animals, are able to smell water, and the smell of this water was like ambrosia to him.

The lion moved closer to the pond, and, as he lowered his head to the water to drink, he suddenly saw his own reflection, thinking it was another lion.

"Oh dear," he said to himself, "I suppose this water belongs to another lion, I should be careful."

He retreated, but soon his thirst drove him back to the water. Again he saw the head of an intimidating lion that stared at him from the surface of the water.

This time our lion thought he might be able to scare the "other lion" away, and he opened his mouth to let out a hair-rising roar. But just as he was showing his teeth, the other lion also opened his mouth and that dangerous sight frightened our lion. He drew back and then came closer again and again, and over and over again he experienced the same thing.

After some time, he became so thirsty and desperate that he said to himself, "Lion or not, I will go now and drink of this water." And truly, as soon as he dipped his face into the water, the other lion vanished.

## The Benefits of Self-Hypnosis

These days, I teach almost all of my client's self-hypnosis, and for most clients this is the first trance experience I offer. After learning self-hypnosis, I provide clients with specific techniques to address their treatment goals, such as pain, allergy, anxiety, or depression management, improved relationships, and improved athletic or artistic performance.

Clients can quickly learn self-hypnosis, which they can continue to use on their own, supported by therapeutic supervision or by using audio recordings or books. This makes it possible to provide many clients, dealing with a variety of therapeutic goals, with "self-hypnotic" homework that allows them to continue their work at home efficiently. As a result, treatment requires fewer sessions. Moreover, this strategy provides clients with a tool that gives them the ability to take control over an effective change strategy, which is empowering; it effectively increases their self-esteem and self-efficacy. Of course, with traditional hypnosis the client ultimately causes any changes himself or herself; but in this case, the client perceives the source of change as coming from the outside, from the hypnotherapist.

## Measures for Preparing and Accommodating the Client

### Accommodating to a Hypnotic State

Just before I begin the self-hypnosis training, I ask the client whether he or she has any experience in autogenic training, Yoga, trance-dance, trance states during sports activities, monotone processes at work, or similar activities. I also sometimes ask about individual abilities or idiosyncrasies that could be important for a later fine-tuning during hypnotic work. But basically I want the client to orientate his or her inner self towards a hypnoid state. When I ask: "How would you describe your deepest state of relaxation during your autogenic training [or whatever trance-like experience they describe]?" the client needs to imagine this state and remember it. This puts him or her associatively closer to a hypnotic state than before I asked this question. These kind of questions are examples of "seeding" or "priming" techniques.

**Sitting Position and Relaxing Posture**

I always teach self-hypnosis training with the client in an upright sitting posture. In my experience, the sitting posture implies a greater sense of personal involvement and a more active personal responsibility than a horizontal posture. I arrange the chairs in a way that I sit next to the client. I suggest a relaxed sitting posture, without crossed legs and with the hands not touching each other. Sometimes I add that this way it will be easier to relax and go into trance. Depending on the client, I might also note that this facilitates dissociation, or I might state proverbs such as, "The right hand does not know what the left is doing" or "The left shall not know what the right is doing." In addition, in my experience it seems easier to transfer self-hypnotic capabilities from sitting position into a lying down than vice versa.

I then describe the structure of the self-hypnosis training to the client. Because of my choice of words, rhythm of speech, and because of the amount of complex information I provide, there is a tendency for clients to go into trance during this introductory section. At the end of this explanation, some clients experience difficulty in keeping their eyes open.

The following is a transcript of a typical self-hypnosis training, beginning with the initial outline, followed by a demonstration of the self-hypnosis induction and the subsequent transition into a hetero-hypnosis experience.

### Transcript of a Self-Hypnosis Training Induction with Commentary

**Clinician: Just look at a spot somewhere. You can choose a spot on the wall or a spot on the carpet. Some people choose to look at the ring on their own hand. Later at home you can discover what works best for you. It is just like when the hypnotist says, "Concentrate on this finger on my hand," or "concentrate on this crystal ball." Hypnosis and self-hypnosis are not only about relaxation but also are about a very high level of concentration on something.**

*[James Braid who introduced the word "hypnosis" later suggested it be changed to monoideism, meaning "concentrated on one thing." So we start here with focusing on just one spot.]*

**Of course, you may change your posture any time you like, to lean back more, to put your head into an even more comfortable position, just following your own personal inner needs…**

*[It is important to give clients the freedom to change to more comfortable body positions whenever necessary for them to remain comfortable.]*

**Before I demonstrate the method to you, I am going to describe it to you briefly. You don't have to memorize everything. You are free to ask me anything afterwards.**

*[By telling the client that he or she does not have to memorize everything, I am communicating that he or she can "just let go."]*

**To begin with, this method contains two parts. In the first part the senses are still oriented to the outside. At the same time, you are looking at the spot I mentioned before. You can choose a spot on your own hand or you can choose a spot on the floor. And then, while you are looking at this spot, you tell yourself four times, what you are seeing.**

**Of course you are only seeing the spot, but in your peripheral vision you can see a lot more while concentrating on only this one spot. So, you see four things. You might say to yourself, for example: I see this spot, I see colors, in the corner of my eyes, I see branches moving, I see the little movement the hand just made.**

**After this you tell yourself four times what you can hear; sounds of the heater in the room, a high sound in the background, a car driving by, voices from far away, and so on.**

**And then four times what you are feeling: all body sensations, temperature of the hands, tension in the shoulders, temperature of the feet, your respiration, swallowing movements, the need to swallow, whatever—whatever comes to your mind. Then the same again with three times seeing, three times hearing, three times feeling; then twice, twice, twice, once, once, once.**

**At this point, you close your eyes. There are a few people for whom it is better to keep their eyes open and continue to concentrate on the spot, but most people are able to concentrate better when their eyes are closed.**

Then the second part begins. You choose a scene, sometime in the past when you felt really relaxed or really safe and secure. It could be the memory of a scene from a wonderful holiday or an experience with a trusted and loved person. And then you pretend to *really be* in this situation right now, as if you were giving a kind of live report from this situation.

In this experience, you use the same pattern as in the first part: four times seeing, four times hearing, four times feeling. You pretend to be at this wonderful holiday place and you are reporting, using this pattern four times seeing, four times hearing, four times feeling, three times, three times, three times... always just silent, inwardly... at home you can do this in a way that works best for you, silent or aloud... this time I will demonstrate it aloud and you will join in silently, inwardly.

I will give you an example of how I typically do the second part myself. I choose a situation from an island where I spent a really wonderful holiday and where I was really relaxed. I pretend to be on this island and give this live report: I see the bare island across the water, I see sailing boats on the water, I see surfers, I see the blue sky.

*[Here, the client is invited to hear what I say and at the same time should do his or her own self-hypnosis. What I see, hear, and feel is only an example. This is similar to the Ericksonian Overload-Technique; it is too much for the conscious mind to process, so the client shifts into a trance state mode.]*

I hear the wind whistling, I hear the smacking of a surfer's sail, I hear the waves, I hear music from the pub in the background.

I feel the wind, I feel the sun, I feel the wind on my skin, I feel the hard stones on the beach, I see the sailing boats, I see...

I will demonstrate this aloud now, while I am sitting next to you, and you will join me, silently, inwardly. What I say will only be an example for you. You yourself will concentrate on what *you* are seeing, hearing, and feeling. In the first part, the experiences will probably be similar of course, the things I see you will probably see as well, for example when a bird flies past the window closely. The sounds will be the same. But the feelings will be different: if I feel my nose itching, you will not necessarily also feel your nose itching. So you will concentrate on the things *you* are seeing, hearing, and feeling. What I say is only an example for the things you might be seeing, hearing, and feeling.

In the second part, I certainly won't know which situation you choose, who is there with you, or whether you are alone, and what feeling safe and secure and comfortable means for you.

So I will leave my inner pictures and I will not tell you about my island again, this would distract you too much. Instead, I will try to help you experience your situation as real and as vividly as possible. In this phase I will not sit exactly parallel to your chair anymore, but I will turn towards you a bit, and you will notice this from the direction of my voice. This way I will be able to attend you better. If I can see there is a good relaxation, I will tell you a story that from my experience helps people to better get into it.

*[Here I tell the client that I will shift away from my own self-hypnosis to support the client in his or her self-hypnosis. My auto-hypnosis slowly is shifting to a hetero-hypnotic state in which I am guiding the client into the client's trance state.]*

**I have told this story to many people before. It is a very nice, positive oriental fairy tale. Some people even say this fairy tale is nicer than our fairy tales. But that's a matter of opinion. Especially in the context of self-hypnosis training I have told this story to many people before, so I am able to tell it differently in this little part or that, depending on the person or the problem. If you like, you can pay a little attention and think about what might be the original story, and "What has he put in especially for me?" Right at the end I will ask you to count from 1 to 20, feeling refreshed and more awake with every number coming back to this room.**

*[Telling the client that I have told this story to many clients before reduces their need to control what is going on. It is not something I am introducing specifically for this client; it is something I often use for many clients. Additionally, I say that it is a very nice and positive story. This seeds the idea for a positive first trance experience.*

*After this, I note that because I told the story before to so many people I can modify it a bit and tailor it to the individual goals of the client; the client can then be curious to see if he or she recognizes what is standard and what is unique. After this, I describe how I will reorient the client at the end of the session.]*

**Do you have any questions?**

**OK. Now we can begin.**

**As I said, I will demonstrate it aloud, four times seeing, hearing, feeling and so on, and you will join me silently, inwardly, using what I say as a starting point.**

**Have you chosen a spot to concentrate on? You can also choose a spot on your hand. I see my spot.**

**I see your movements. I still see this spot. I see the colors in the room,**

**I hear different sounds in the room... still sounds, something cracking, voices in the background...**

**I feel my hands... my hands' temperature, one a little warmer than the other, my feet solidly on the ground...**

> *[Through modeling, I direct the client's attention to the outside by inviting him or her to note four things I (and he or she) can see, four things they hear, and four things they feel. Then, three things, two things, and finally one thing they hear, see, and feel.]*

**I still see this spot... The colors are getting a little brighter... and still a little brighter... Sounds of someone walking about... and again this high sound... the beginning of a relaxation in the shoulders... pleasant feelings... feelings of warmth... more and more relaxation...**

**And still this spot... soft movements from the branches outside the window.**

**Some rustling sound from far away... it is quiet in the house...**

**different body sensations... the shoulders are beginning to relax...**

**And this spot... stepping sounds... different body sensations...**

**To finally close my eyes…**

*[Usually by this time, my voice is changing more and more to a quiet trance voice, based on my own process of going into a trance state myself.]*

**and take myself into this situation, pleasant memories, concentrating on them… on these inner pictures… feelings… of comfort and security and taking your time… four times seeing, four times hearing, four times feeling…**

*[Here, I begin to direct the client's attention to his or her inner experience of a nice memory. This is the second step. We proceed, again, by seeing, hearing, and feeling four times, three times, two times, and one time.]*

**and for some people, fragments emerge… from different situations… and for now, this technique is a standard technique. You can use it to develop your very own technique… to become even calmer, even more relaxed by seeing, hearing, feeling, …**

*[Utilizing here the client's own memories.]*

**and if I might be talking about hearing and you are still busy seeing or continue to feel, you might hear a voice in the background… like a car radio or like music from a neighbor's apartment… the music is playing in the background, *but if there is something important on the radio*… then you can hear it… if not, then it stays in the background… and you concentrate on the things you are seeing, hearing and feeling… at your own pace… as long as you want to… and of course I do not know whether right now you are seeing or hearing or feeling… and this is not important at all, because my voice is casually playing in the background… and you can still notice everything,**

**like on the car radio, the important traffic news... you can notice all that and then again your thoughts and feelings... and the conscious mind, the head can often only do one thing at a time, while the unconscious, the back room of the head, that part that you dream with, can do many different things at a time, and so you are able to see, hear, feel in this pleasant situation and at the same time listen to this nice story...**

*[Here I allow my client to be distracted, if this is what they experience. He or she does not have to hear me consciously—like a car radio while driving a car, the client can hear my voice or sometimes not hear my voice... BUT IF THERE IS SOMETHING IMPORTANT ON THE RADIO... This I say with a different tone of voice, and in this way emphasizing—whenever I speak in this voice—that what I am saying is important. The client is therefore more likely to hear and process the idea.]*

**and one part of you might be curious about which part of the story is new and especially for me and my aim, and which part is just this wonderful old fairy tale...**

*[Curiosity is used to focus attention but also I note that there are special parts in the story—tailored especially for the client and his or her goals.]*

**because the conscious mind has one language and the unconscious mind has another. The conscious mind thinks in logical sentences and the unconscious in images. This story about the lion...**

**Your conscious mind can have an intellectual interest in analyzing the story, while the unconscious can concentrate on your therapeutic goal(s)... the conscious mind might sometimes notice incorrect grammar, while the**

**unconscious mind is hearing only the content... and this lion lives in the forest... and of course the conscious mind knows, lions do not live in forests.**

*[This conscious/unconscious differentiation is especially helpful for very controlled clients for facilitating the process of letting go. It allows them to use the conscious mind to analyze the situation and at the same time hypnosis can still work.]*

**It is a fairy tale... in this fairy tale the lion lives in the forest... and this beautiful oriental story... and maybe the conscious interest enjoys analyzing how these oriental stories are different from Western fairy tales... this positive, solution-oriented content...**

**and the lion in this forest, in which it is windy all the time... there is this permanent sound in this forest... and the lion hears the sound and does not hear it... in the background this permanent rushing... so familiar to the lion already... he hears the rushing and does not hear it... it is like music... It is always windy in this forest... one of the reasons he stays in the forest is this watering hole... containing this amazingly refreshing water... but because of the constant wind in the forest, the water's surface is always rippled...**

*[For some clients it is important to emphasize the fairy tale style of the story so the rational part of thinking does not interfere with unconscious reasoning.]*

**the water never reflects anything... and one day the lion goes hunting...**

*[Here the image of the mirror indirectly is introduced. It is a priming/seeding of the idea of a mirror that shows up later in the story.]*

**and from minute to minute the lion becomes more and more focused, he has a goal, he becomes more and more absorbed, focused... and only his goal... he sees his goal before his eyes... he smells his goal, he feels his goal, he hears his goal... more and more... and more and more... he hears the wind and does not hear it... he smells the wood and does not smell it... more and more absorbed... more able to concentrate... with dreamlike certainty, more and more focused, absorbed... he sees the trees and does not see them... with dreamlike confidence he runs between the trees... totally absorbed and focused... on his goal... at first he still feels his body... and more and more... only the goal... and eventually he runs out of the forest... into the desert... and there is the sun, and it is warm,**

*[The attention of the client is more and more focused, and at the same time the focus is directed on the client's therapeutic goal(s).]*

**but he feels the heat and does not feel it... he hears the different sounds in the desert and does not hear them... he sees the animals and does not see them... he concentrates on his goal... he smells the desert and does not smell it... he feels his body and does not feel it... but eventually... eventually they will come back...**

*[The suggestion of seeing without seeing, hearing without hearing, etc., are indirect suggestions for highly focused attention—a trance state with negative hallucinations on several sensory channels.]*

**coming back... coming back—his needs...**

*["Coming back, coming back," this is spoken in the different "commanding" tone; and interspersion technique that contains embedded commands. Here I suggest the possibility of a*

*reorientation from a trance state, but at the same time that the client does not want to "come back," and because of this the next suggestion of "feeling thirsty" will be followed easily. This is a subtle deepening technique via fractionation. Many clients are swallowing at this point in the story.]*

**he is thirsty... he is really thirsty... terribly thirsty... the long hunt, the heat in the desert... the dry air... thirst... and he is far away from his watering hole... of course he can walk back to his watering hole... he has enough resources...**

*[This has two meanings: (1) the meaning in the story of going back to the lion's own lake and (2) it is always possible to reorient from trance state.]*

***He has enough will and enough control and power... it is always possible to come back* but he is thirsty *now*...**

*[Some clients may be feeling anxious about the urge to swallow. To address this, I also mention "enough will, enough control," and "it is always possible to come back."]*

**lions are able to smell... smell water... and there is water, very close to where he is now... fresh water... and thirsty and smelling this water and going there... and there is this little lake... a deep blue, calm, no wind, as smooth as glass... and walking down to it...**

**But as soon as he lowers his head towards the surface, there is this other lion, and he draws back, startled... he backs out and lies down in the shadow beneath this tree and waits... eventually the other one will leave, "I only have to wait..." But a few minutes later, lowering the head towards the water, the other one is there again... and he**

**starts feeling annoyed at himself... because he got himself into this situation so recklessly...**

*[Seeing the face in the water. This is the core of the story. Being frightened by his own face, thinking it is somebody else.]*

**of course... he can walk back, he has enough strength... he can go back anytime... but he is thirsty right now, he wants to drink right now... it is now that he feels his needs... and he is getting so angry at the other lion because he will not go away... and he runs down and roars and thunders and rumbles... and he rips open his mouth as far as a lion possibly can rip his mouth open... but the other lion rips his mouth open just as far... obviously just as far... obviously... as he tries it the fourth time... a helpless, frightened lion is looking at him... and this makes himself feel desperate and helpless... and he lies down in the shadow again and does not know what to do... somehow the situation feels strangely familiar... it feels as if he can go neither back nor forth... although he actually knows he could go back to his own water... and actually he could also go to this fresh water here... to this lake as smooth as glass...**

*[Here I again offer the idea that it is possible to reorient and come back whenever it is necessary. This increases the probability that the client will cooperate and respond.]*

**and still he feels as if he was paralyzed... strangely familiar... and he closes his eyes and does not know what to do... he is helpless... and then he is surprised, very unexpectedly he sees beautiful images.... And his head says, actually those pictures do not fit this situation... somewhere... deep inside... beautiful images... from way back... he is hunting butterflies... he never caught any of**

**the butterflies... but that doesn't matter... he is totally at ease... he can wait... he takes his time... he observes... he sees the butterflies... and sneaks up... millimeter after millimeter... hour after hour... same and same again... he sneaks up, and every time again he is sure, this time it will work... and he jumps and the butterfly flies away... hour after hour... ten times... twenty times... forty times... day after day... that is like a time, in which there aren't any mistakes... he does not know exactly yet, how much he knows... he doesn't even know how much he is learning in this situation... hour after hour he is sneaking up... only sees his goal... his whole body is focused ... his eyes... millimeter after millimeter... a relaxed tension... an absorbed relaxing tension... even though his body trembles with excitement a little... he is absolutely relaxed... it is a time, when there are no mistakes... only curiosity... and experimenting... and he jumps... the butterfly flies away... hour after hour... and as he opens his eyes and moves, he sees the lake... a lake like the sea... seeing the sea... smooth as glass, a deep blue, calm air... and he gets up and slowly strolls towards the lake...**

*[In addressing this state of paralysis and helplessness, I am reorienting the client back to a childhood resource. This should be done in a way that does not elicit thoughts or feelings associated with childhood trauma via this feeling of helplessness. So I address the surprise of the lion, when he unexpectedly sees or experiences positive memories from the past.]*

**it is this special way of powerful strolling... he moves sinuously, he has the full strength of an adult lion, the right posture... in the shoulders, the hips, in his neck... he has the full strength and experience of a big, adult lion... and at the same time it is like an idea... as if an idea of the**

**young lion was inside of him... he walks just a little bit differently... strolls just a little bit differently... and shortly before he reaches the lake... he hears a voice, as if it came from the outside... lion or not lion... his own voice, he is startled... by his own voice... lion or not...**

*[Here the power and life experiences of the adult lion are combined with the creativity and curiosity of the young lion.]*

**and he lowers his face into the water, the water ripples... he drinks this cool water and breathes... relieved... and the water is so refreshing... enjoying... and he drinks at his own pace... delightedly... and nothing else matters right now...]**

*[Symbolically, the suggestion is to let go; and by drinking water overcoming the fear and going to a trance state.]*

**he feels calmer and calmer... and the calmer he feels the smoother the water gets... sometimes he can see the other lion... sometimes he twists his face into a grimace, like the other one... sometimes he smiles, in a quick change... and all he hears is lion or not... and he lies down in the shade again... and the cool water refreshes the body... the long hunt... it is pleasant... a mixture of comfortable tiredness and feeling refreshed... a well-earned tiredness...**

**and so he starts walking home...**

*[This feeling of letting go is deepened now.]*

**he reaches his home, his own watering hole, his forest... and he hears the wind and the permanent rushing... and he lies down at his *usual spot... and he has the feeling that there have been a lot of interesting events on this day... and he feels he now deserves to just BE, here, now... and he hears the wind and the steady rushing* of the wind, like music...**

**and he hears the birds in a different way than before... and he smells the forest in a different way than before... and more and more he just IS, here, now... he doesn't know if he should call it meditation... he just IS, here, now... maybe without any wishes right now... without any interests and without needs...**

**and later he did not know if it was a long time or a brief time or if a brief time was a long time...**

**before you can start to count...**

**Reaching home, his very safe place, and going deeper and deeper...**

**from 1 to 20 and with each number you reorient yourself more and—after having stored this deep state of relaxation... so that whenever you are doing self-hypnosis you can remember this feeling—this state—of deep relaxation and because it is stored inside you can reorient now by counting from 1 to 20.**

*[Before reorientation the client is asked to memorize and store this deep trance state so he or she can go back to this whenever it is necessary.]*

### Debriefing After the Self-Hypnosis Training Experience

Usually, when clients return from this first trance experience, they are amazed at how deeply relaxed they feel. This also includes those clients who had warned me in advance that until now they have had great difficulties with "letting go" and that hypnosis "probably won't work" for them.

Sometimes clients tell me about their experiences, about differences in their body awareness. Many report time distortion experiences, feeling that the whole process of 20 to 25 minutes was only 3 to 15 minutes.

Sometimes after the first session, a client may ask, "When I do self-hypnosis, what should I do when the part with the lion comes, should I tell the story to myself?" I emphasize that the story itself is not needed to be a part of self-hypnosis. I told the story because from my experience it helps clients to achieve a useful state and that there were certain elements woven into the story that will facilitate achievement of the previously defined therapeutic goal.

I ask the clients to watch out for positive changes that occur between this session and the next, so we will be able to build on those changes. I add that of course the clients may remember parts of the story during their training at home and also remember my voice or the images that appeared to them during the session or maybe that they will remember the feeling of the chair in my office. If so, this can help them to go into trance quicker and easier and to feel more secure.

## Outline of the Self-Hypnosis Training Session

### Outlining the Method

Using hypnotic speech patterns to orient the client to a hypnotic state:

### Demonstrating the Technique

Concentrating with open eyes on an object/point in the room:

- 4 times visual, 4 times auditory, 4 times kinesthetic
- 3 times visual, 3 times auditory, 3 times kinesthetic
- 2 times visual, 2 times auditory, 2 times kinesthetic
- 1 time visual, 1 time auditory 1, time kinesthetic

Closing the eyes. Remembering a situation in the past when you have been very relaxed and safe.

- 4 times visual, 4 times auditory, 4 times kinesthetic
- 3 times visual, 3 times auditory, 3 times kinesthetic
- 2 times visual, 2 times auditory, 2 times kinesthetic
- 1 time visual, 1 time auditory, 1 time kinesthetic

The Lion Story

Reorientation

Counting from 1 to 20 and returning to the current setting.

**References**

Holtz, K. L., Mrochen, S., Nemetschek, P., & Trenkle, B. (2007). *Neugierig aufs Großwerden: Praxis der Hypnotherapie mit Kindern und Jugendlichen* [*Becoming curious: Hypnotherapy with children and adolescents*]. Heidelberg, Germany: Carl-Auer.

Mrochen, S., Holtz, K. L., & Trenkle, B. (1993). *Die Pupille des Bettnässers: Hypnotherapeutische Arbeit mit Kindern und Jugendlichen* [*The pupil of a bedwetter: Hypnotherapeutic work with children and adolescents*]. Heidelberg, Germany: Carl-Auer.

Shah, I. (1978). *A perfumed scorpion: A way to the way.* London: Octagon Press.

Trenkle, B. (1986). Ansätze zur Fokussierung therapeutischer Interventionen und Stärkung der Therapiemotivation [Approaches in focusing therapeutic interventions and strengthening client motivation for therapy]. *Hypnose und Kognition, 3,* 29–35.

Trenkle, B. (1988). Charles Van Riper meets Milton H. Erickson: Approaches in the treatment of the adult stutterer. In S. R. Lankton, J. K. Zeig (Eds.), *Treatment of special populations with Ericksonian approaches* (pp. 54–68). Philadelphia, PA: Brunner/Mazel.

Trenkle, B. (1994). The Ericksonian utilization approach for the rehabilitation of paralyzed patients. In J. K. Zeig (Ed.), *Ericksonian methods: The essence of the story* (pp. 445–461). Philadelphia, PA: Brunner/Mazel.

Trenkle, B. (1997). *Die Löwen-Geschichte: Hypnotisch-metaphorische Kommunikation und Selbsthypnosetraining* [*The Lion Story: Hypnotic-metaphorical communication and self-hypnosis*]. Heidelberg, Germany: Carl-Auer.

Trenkle, B. (2001). *The ha-ha handbook: A seriously funny collection of jokes from here, there, and everywhere*. Phoenix, AZ: Zeig, Tucker, & Theisen.

Trenkle, B. (2007). *Das zweite Ha-Handbuch der Witze zu Hypnose und Psychotherapie* [*The second ha-handbook of jokes about hypnosis and psychotherapy*]. Heidelberg, Germany: Carl-Auer.

Trenkle, B. (2008). *Das Aha!-Handbuch der Aphorismen und Sprüche für Therapie, Beratung und Hängematte* [*The Aha!-Handbook of aphorisms and sayings for therapy, advice, and support*]. Heidelberg, Germany: Carl-Auer.

# CHAPTER 12

# The Modified Steeple Technique and the GR Wicks Induction

**Allan M. Cyna**

*Allan M. Cyna trained in the UK as a general practitioner and then in anesthesiology in the United Kingdom; Baltimore, USA; and Australia. He is currently senior specialist anesthesiologist at the Women's and Children's Hospital, Adelaide, and Nepean Hospital, Sydney; clinical associate professor, University of Sydney; director of studies, South Australian Society of Hypnosis; and chair, Communication in Anaesthesia Special Interest Group of the Australian and New Zealand College of Anaesthetists. Dr. Cyna is an author and peer reviewer for the Cochrane collaboration and has a PhD in hypnosis for pain relief in childbirth. He has published a number of articles on the use of hypnosis and hypnotic language in the medical setting and is editor-in-chief of the leading book on this topic (*Handbook of Communication in Anaesthesia and Critical Care, *published by Oxford University Press; Cyna, Andrew, & Tan, 2011).*

* * *

For any hypnosis technique to be therapeutic, it is essential to develop patient rapport. Most perioperative interactions usually involve an implementation of explicit or implicit language structures, such as the LAURS (listening, acceptance, utilization, reframing, and suggestion) of communication (Cyna et al., 2011). Listening for meaning and potential areas for subsequent or future utilization is an essential first step. Acceptance of where the patient is enhances rapport and allows for subsequent interactions to be facilitated and optimized. Utilization, for example a favorite activity, can frequently be integrated into the induction or reframed into something therapeutic.

For example, a patient immediately prior to anesthesia expressed that she was terrified and wanted to get away. The anesthesiologist said, "If you went away somewhere more comfortable for you, where would you get away to?"

**Patient**: I'd climb the hill overlooking my house.

**Anesthesiologist**: OK, Close your eyes. Take a deep relaxing breath in and, as you breathe out let me know when you get there. What can you hear?... What's the temperature? The humidity?... What can you feel?... What can you see?... and each time you breathe out you can feel yourself relax a little bit more.

**Patient**: I can see all the lights flickering. It's beautiful!

Utilizing unhelpful thoughts and concerns can often be reframed in the form of a suggestion. As illustrated above, concerns need to be validated and they then can be reframed in the form of a suggestion.

In another example, one of my anesthesiology colleagues was interacting with a patient who had severe needle phobia despite also having nipple rings and multiple tattoos. The patient said, "If you come near me with that needle, I'll die!" Rather than attempting to reassure the patient by saying "It is just a small needle" or "It's no worse than the tattoos that you have had done," she used the LAURS concept by saying, "That's OK (acceptance)... Why don't you just let that arm die (utilization) for just a moment (reframe)," accepting and utilizing the patient's words and reframing them to a metaphorical—and limited—"dying" of the arm for "just a moment." The suggestion not only restricted the dying to a body part (the arm) but also facilitated dissociation by using "that arm" rather than "your arm" in the suggestion. At this point the patient's arm went transiently limp as the suggestion for arm anesthesia was realized. A 16G intravenous cannula was inserted comfortably while the arm stayed cataleptic during the procedure. This example illustrates that patients, when stressed, can rapidly respond to suggestions eliciting complex hypnotic phenomena such as arm catalepsy and anesthesia that can facilitate therapy without a formal hypnotic induction.

The LAURS concept can be used as an integral part of any medical history and examination. However, when using hypnosis more formally, it is essential to address both conscious and unconscious factors that could lead to resistance, such as a history of a bad experience of hypnosis, fear of loss of control, or fear of disclosing private information.

Rapport and motivation are also key. Fortunately, most patients presenting to anesthesiologists are already highly motivated to reduce both pain and anxiety, permitting a relatively easy hypnotic induction. In the context of perioperative care, the modified steeple and the Wicks rapid induction are two of my favorite induction techniques and are ideal for clinicians who require rapid inductions—for example in a busy clinic when something simple, quick, and easy to learn is required. Both induction techniques begin with a short seeding where the patient is asked to do three things when they are ready to rapidly relax and go into hypnosis. The modified steeple is more commonly used as patients do not need to be particularly hypnotizable for the induction to have, at least, some beneficial effect. In addition, this technique has the advantage of subsequent use as a self-hypnosis technique for patients to practice at home.

### The Modified Steeple Technique

The modified steeple is a rapid induction of hypnosis that can be taught to patients in approximately 5 to 10 minutes in the clinic or preoperative ward prior to surgery. Patrick McCarthy, a GP in Wellington, New Zealand, introduced me to this technique, and it is one that I frequently use in the preanesthetic clinic to variable, but often excellent, effect. It typically takes a single session for patients to achieve enough proficiency to practice this self-hypnosis technique at home. The induction works particularly well in the anxious patient who cannot concentrate, as it involves a physical behavioral truism as an integral part of the process. This apparent nonvolitional response often generates surprise, and sometimes confusion, thus enhancing the realization of suggestions that follow. Patients who are considered suitable are asked whether they would be interested in learning a self-hypnosis technique. They are informed that it takes about 5 minutes to learn and is usually ten to twenty times more powerful than a pharmacological premedication (suggestion). It is superficially a very simple technique to teach and learn, but has some interesting aspects that allow most subjects, clients, or patients to go into a light (but on occasion deep) trance relatively easily and quickly. It relies on a series of physiological truisms with embedded suggestions. The response of the patient then dictates the pace and language utilized for deepening and subsequently eliciting ideo-motor responses.

### The Preamble to Both Induction Techniques

The patient is informed that hospitals are noisy places and,

> While everybody else is getting on with what they need to do, keeping you safe and comfortable… it is an opportunity for you to take some time out and relax… paying attention to only what is useful for you… whether it is focusing on what you are doing or taking on board anything helpful… that can then be available to you in the future when needed.

## A Description of the Modified Steeple Technique

The technique is taught in three parts and involves three components. The first part is a demonstration with the patient/client just watching. The second part involves talking the patient/client through the induction as they actually do it. The third part involves watching the patient/client perform the induction technique without interruption from the therapist during the process.

The three components of this induction begin by asking the patient to clasp both hands and fingers (Figure 1) with palms held firmly together and fingers interlaced. The second step is to ask the patient to straighten their two index fingers so that they are separated while still leaving the remaining fingers and two hands otherwise clasped together. The patient is then asked to focus their gaze on the space between the two index fingers when straightened. A small distance of about three cms should separate the index fingers initially, with the remaining fingers locked together as the hands otherwise remain tightly clasped (Figure 2). The patient is then told that, "The two index fingers will seem to come together all on their own without thinking about it, as if there is a magnetic attraction between a 'north pole' finger and 'south pole' finger."

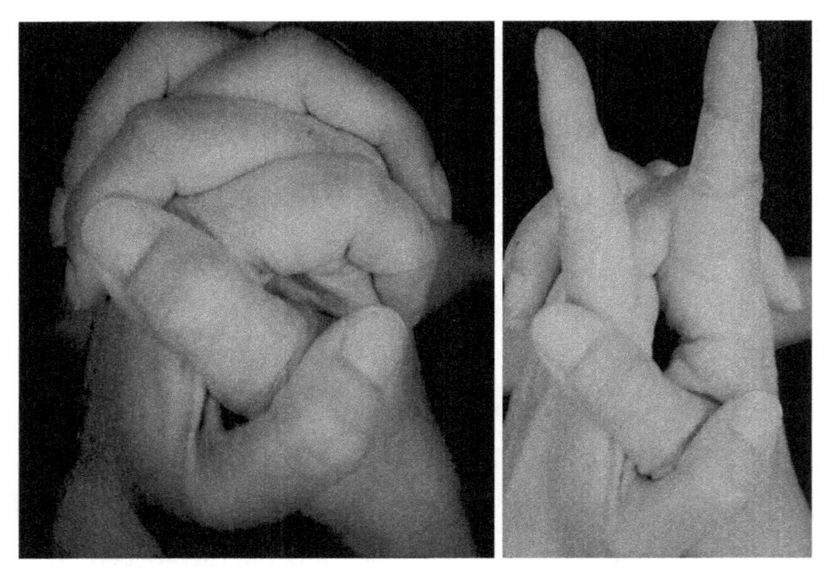

*Figure 1. Steeple Technique: hands clasped together.*
*Figure 2. Steeple Technique: index fingers about 3 cm apart.*

The fingers actually come together because of the tension placed on the lumbrical muscles and this physiological truism encourages subsequent nonvolitional responses to suggestion. "As soon as the tips of the index fingers touch" (Figure 3), you can initiate the third step by asking the patient to,

> Close the eyes… take a deep breath in and hold it for 5 seconds and then… as you breathe out you can feel yourself blowing away tension

into the atmosphere... as if a balloon is collapsing... as you breathe out.

*Figure 3. Steeple Technique: the tips of the index fingers touching (after seeming to come together automatically).*

The exhalation to functional residual capacity (FRC) is another physiological truism which allows for a "yes set" to be developed each time the patient breathes out. FRC is the point in the breathing cycle (at the end of a normal exhalation breath) where the muscles of the diaphragm and chest wall are in the neutral position with both diaphragm and intercostals at their most relaxed. As the patient breathes out a normal breath to end tidal ventilation, the chest wall muscles are maximally relaxed, and this is usually noticed subconsciously generating a subconscious "yes" each time a patient breathes out.

As a suggestion is given indirectly to focus on breathing, the subject soon begins to appreciate subconsciously that each time they breathe out the chest wall relaxes. By the time they have breathed out three to five breaths, a nonvolitional subconscious relaxation response often generalizes to the rest of the body.

> Each time you breathe out from now on you will relax even more... breathe in some strength and control you didn't even know that you had and ... each time you breathe out blow away anything you don't like into the atmosphere as you feel yourself relax... nothing you need to think about... nothing you need to try and do... as it just seems to happen all on its own...

Each time the patient breathes out, he or she can be given suggestions to reinforce the relaxation suggestion, such as, "That's right," "Well done," "That's good," "Excellent," and "You are doing really well."

Once the patient has closed his or her eyes, the patient can be directed to "allow the hands to relax comfortably on the lap" (if sitting) or "abdomen" (if lying down). Deepening suggestions can be utilized as progressive relaxation or guided favorite place imagery with a suggestion to utilize all the senses noticing the temperature, humidity, colors, sights, and sounds of the place whether it be somewhere relaxing on holiday or somewhere comfortable at home.

After the initial demonstration with the patient watching, the modified steeple technique is then conducted while taking the patient through each step. Finally, the patient is asked to perform the technique with the therapist remaining silent so that they can reassure themselves (and the therapist) that they can do this at home any time they wish to do so. The suggestion is then given that the more people practice the easier it becomes, the more rapidly they enter trance, and the more effective and useful the technique will become. It can also be suggested that:

> At some point the physical process of clasping the fingers is no longer required. Indeed, there comes a point where, as soon as you imagine yourself performing the technique you will suddenly relax and enter trance rapidly without thinking about it or physically doing anything else.

Protective suggestions are given that the patient will only go into trance when it is useful to them for their own health and welfare consistent with the advice of a trained healthcare professional. Just before trance termination, the following suggestion can be given:

> You now know that, you will be able to do this technique any time you want to... be it at home or wherever or whenever the need arises... Like anything when we practice something it becomes easier to use and more effective for you.

### The GR Wicks Rapid Induction Technique

The GR Wicks rapid induction has been perfected by Dr. Graham R. Wicks, who is one of Australia's national treasures and a past President of the Australian Society of Hypnosis. Dr. Wicks has practiced as a medical clinical hypnotherapist for over 35 years at the Women's and Children's Hospital in Adelaide, Australia.

Following the usual explanation of hypnosis and medical history, this rapid induction technique begins with a question put to the patient. "Would you prefer to go into hypnosis extremely rapidly or moderately quickly?" This double bind usually leads to rapid patient responses if one of these choices is acceptable. The technique then requires the clinician to obtain permission to gently touch and hold the patient's wrist lightly between thumb and index finger. The wrist is then gently lifted to shoulder level with the following suggestion. "Close your eyes... take a deep breath... and... hold it." As the words "hold it" are spoken, the hand and arm should come to a rest elevated and very lightly supported by the index finger and thumb of the practitioner's hand (see Figure 4 below).

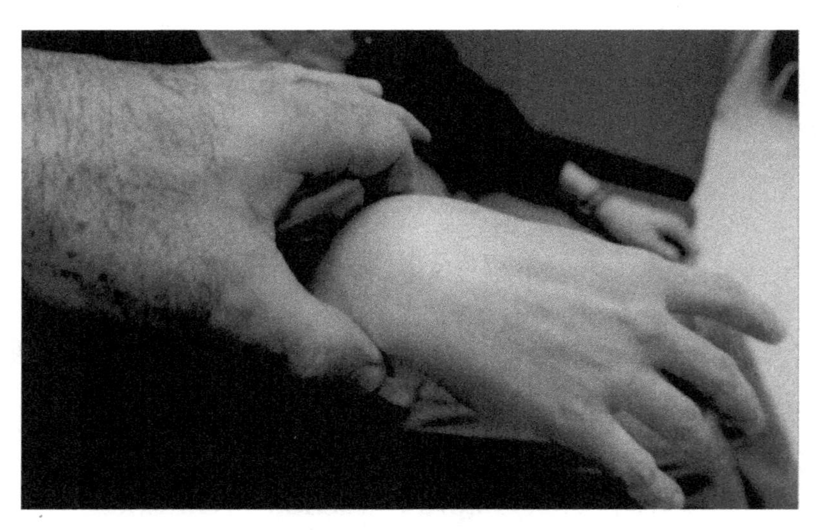

*Figure 4. The Wicks Induction: the patient's hand and arm gently supported by the index finger and thumb of the practitioner's hand just prior to release.*

The confusion generated is that the "hold it" suggestion is unclear as to whether this refers to the breath or the arm levitation. There are three possible responses at this stage. Either the hand becomes cataleptic and stays in that position, or it starts to float up, or starts falling to the lap. The patient's response determines which phrase is then used. If the hand falls, the suggestion is for the arm to come to rest comfortably on the lap and as the arm comes gently to rest on the lap the patient can relax even more until they "... start feeling as relaxed as is just right for you just now." As the hand comes to rest on the lap the therapist can then suggest that "... you can start to feel as comfortable as you would like to feel for just now."

If the arm looks like it might levitate, the suggestion is for the arm to start:

> ... feeling lighter and lighter and... the lighter the arm feels... the more relaxed you can feel and the more relaxed you feel... the lighter the arm will become. Almost as if some string or ribbon is attached to the wrist leading to one or more helium balloons gently pulling on the wrist as the arm floats up feeling lighter and lighter.

## In Summary

These two techniques easily lend themselves to allow the practitioner to guide patients into further deepening techniques if required. They are also useful in gauging how rapidly patients are likely to accept suggestions in the clinical context and will provide a qualitative assessment of hypnotizability. We frequently set up ideomotor finger signals as described by Cheek (1994), which can facilitate further interactions in hypnosis including lived-in or believed-in imagination for minor or major surgery as the sole or adjunctive technique.

## References

Cheek, D. B. (1994). *Hypnosis: The application of ideomotor techniques*. Needham, MA: Allyn and Bacon.

Cyna, A. M., Andrew, M. I., & Tan, S.G.M. (2011). Structures. In A. M. Cyna, M. I. Andrew, S.G.M. Tan, & A. P. Smith (Eds.), *Handbook of communication in anaesthesia and critical care* (pp. 17-29). Oxford, UK: Oxford University Press.

## For Further Reading...

Cyna, A. M., Tomkins, D., Maddock, T., & Barker, D. (2007). Brief hypnosis for severe needle phobia using switch-wire imagery in a 5-year old. *Paediatric Anaesthesia, 17,* 800-804.

Lang, E. V., & Laser, E. (2011). *Patient sedation without medication.* North Charleston, SC: CreateSpace.

Mackenzie, A. (2014). *Everybody stay calm.* Lilydale, Australia: Global Publishing Group.

Wong, L., Cyna, A. M., & Matthews, G. (2011). Rapid hypnosis as an anaesthesia adjunct for evacuation of postpartum vulval haematoma. *Australia and New Zealand Journal of Obstetrics & Gynaecology, 51,* 265-267.

# ABOUT THE EDITOR

Mark P. Jensen, Ph.D., is a Professor and Vice Chair for Research at the Department of Rehabilitation Medicine, University of Washington, in Seattle, Washington, USA. He has been studying chronic pain and helping individuals better manage chronic pain for over 30 years. He has been funded by the National Institutes of Health and other agencies to study the efficacy and mechanisms of various treatments for chronic pain, including hypnosis. He has published extensively (six books and over 450 articles and book chapters) on the topics of pain assessment and treatment.

He has received numerous awards for his writing and scientific contributions including the 2004 Roy M. Dorcus award for Best Clinical Paper from the Society of Clinical and Experimental Hypnosis, the 2009 Clark L. Hull award for Scientific Excellence in Writing from the American Society of Clinical Hypnosis, and the 2012 American Psychological Association Division 30 Award for Distinguished Contributions to Scientific Hypnosis.

His book on the use of hypnosis for chronic pain management, *Hypnosis for chronic pain: Therapist guide,* published by Oxford University Press, won the 2011 Society of Clinical and Experimental Hypnosis Arthur Shapiro Award for Best Book on Hypnosis. He is also a popular international speaker and workshop facilitator.

CPSIA information can be obtained
at www.ICGtesting.com
Printed in the USA
LVHW081956110921
697438LV00015B/574